What is in Authentic Reading Practice?

The real world requires the use of many varied reading skills. Citizens must be able to locate information, comprehend what is read, and then act appropriately. Students must be taught the skills needed to fill out a job application, understand an ad, assemble a toy, or gather information from a magazine article. *Authentic Reading Practice* provides this skill practice, starting your students on their real-life reading adventure.

Using Authentic Reading Practice

- Each section may be used independently of the others.
- Teacher pages at the beginning of each section describe the activities and offer suggestions for their use.
- Introduce a skill with a guided lesson before asking students to practice independently. Reproducing the lessons on an overhead transparency will assist you in presenting a skill to the entire class.
- Assessment checklists are provided for each section. Use these to check specific behaviors observed, note special problems, and to plan lessons in areas of need.
- The models and practice pages presented in this book are only the beginning. Once students understand a skill, provide additional practice using materials from real life.

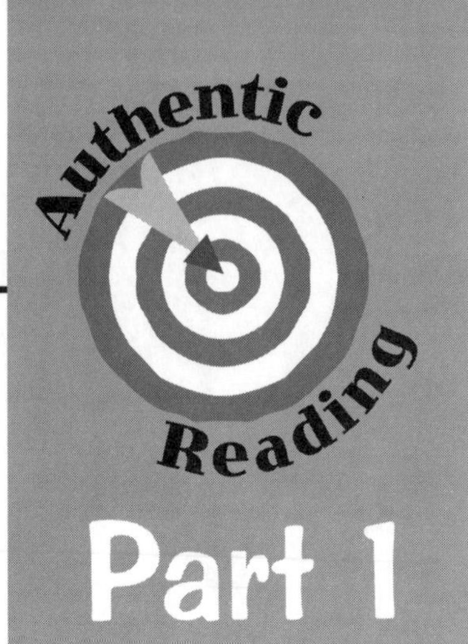

Everyday Reading Skills

Every day we put our reading skills to work—we look up a telephone number, order from a catalog, or follow directions to make something. The activities in this section provide practice with these varied real-life skills.

It's always preferable to use "real" materials. Enlist student help in gathering forms and applications that interest them. Make overhead transparencies of these forms and fill them in as a class. As students become more experienced, assign pages from this book for independent practice.

Reading Pictures

Graphic elements—drawings, photographs, diagrams, and so on—are important sources of information. This section includes observing and evaluating, interpreting information, and following directions.

ACTIVITIES

Reading Diagrams (Pages 4 and 5)
Students study a diagram of a water purification plant and answer questions about the diagram.

Track-and-Field (Pages 6–8)
Students use pictures to determine placing at a track-and-field meet.

Pinwheel (Page 9)
Students follow picture directions to make a paper pinwheel.

Water Purification

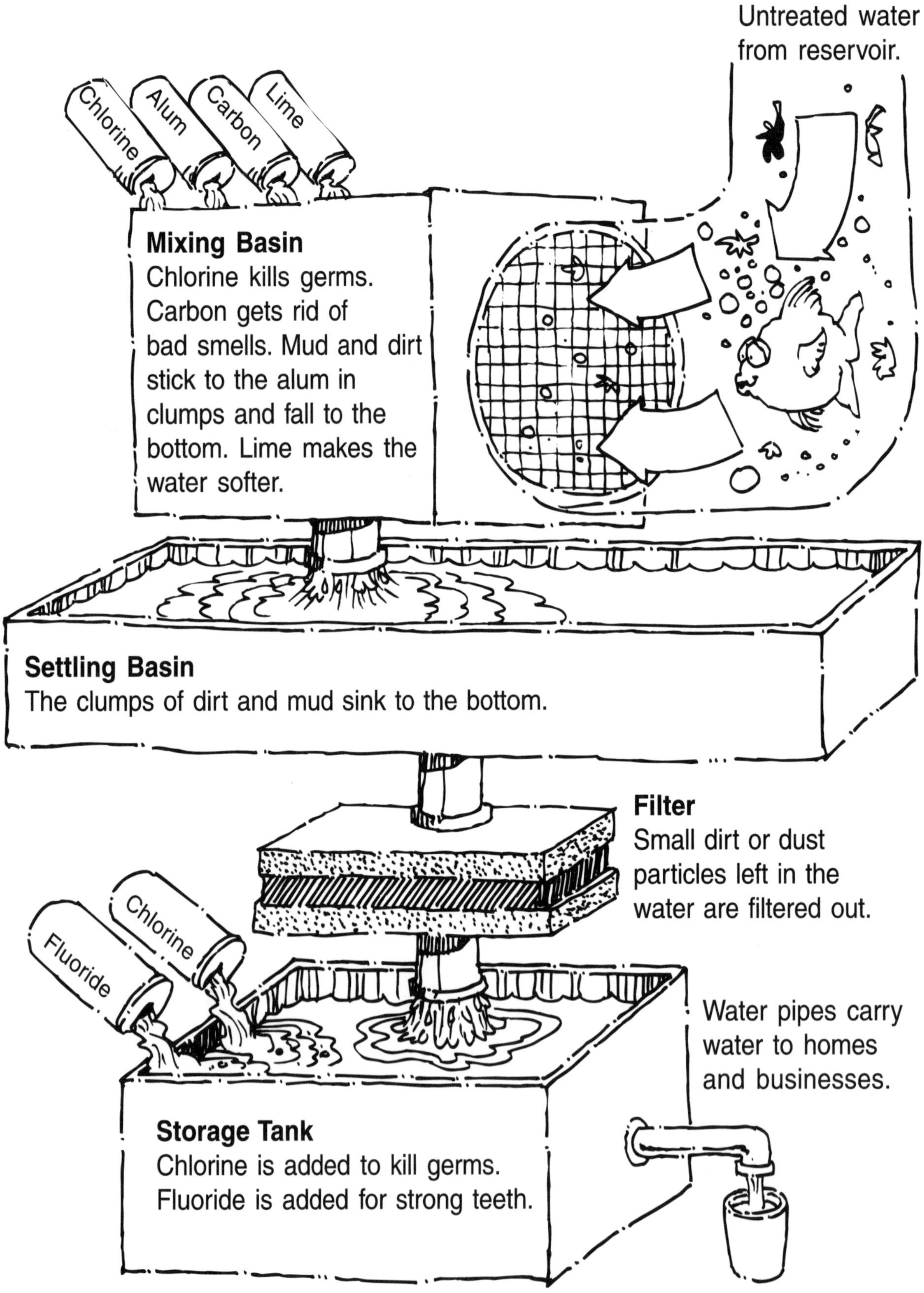

Untreated water from reservoir.

Chlorine

Alum

Carbon

Lime

Mixing Basin
Chlorine kills germs. Carbon gets rid of bad smells. Mud and dirt stick to the alum in clumps and fall to the bottom. Lime makes the water softer.

Settling Basin
The clumps of dirt and mud sink to the bottom.

Filter
Small dirt or dust particles left in the water are filtered out.

Chlorine

Fluoride

Storage Tank
Chlorine is added to kill germs. Fluoride is added for strong teeth.

Water pipes carry water to homes and businesses.

Name:

Reading Diagrams

Examine the diagram showing the process of water purification. Read the captions. Then answer the questions about the process by which water is made pure enough to drink.

1. Where does the untreated water come from?

____

2. What is added to the water in the storage tank? Why?

____

____

3. How are mud and dirt removed from the water? Where does this occur?

____

____

4. List the four stages in water purification illustrated in this diagram.

______________ ______________

______________ ______________

5. Using what you have learned from this diagram, explain why it is important to purify water before it is used as drinking water.

____

____

____

Name:

Track-and-Field

Students from Anderson and Taylor High Schools are competing in a track meet. Study the pictures and information below and fill in the missing information on this sheet and sheet 2. Then answer the questions on sheet 3.

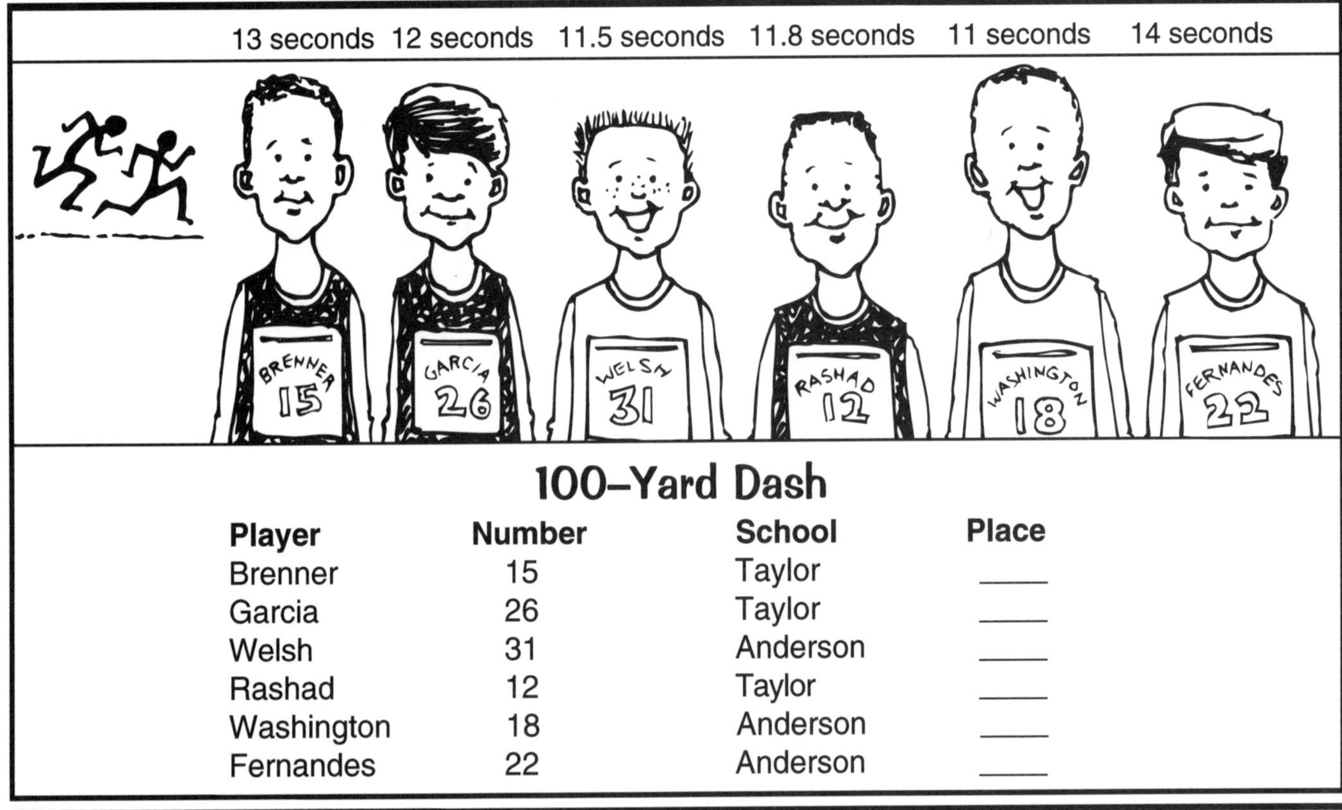

100-Yard Dash

Player	Number	School	Place
Brenner	15	Taylor	_____
Garcia	26	Taylor	_____
Welsh	31	Anderson	_____
Rashad	12	Taylor	_____
Washington	18	Anderson	_____
Fernandes	22	Anderson	_____

High Jump

Player	Number	School	Place
Evans	_____	Taylor	_____
Macpherson	_____	Taylor	_____
Washington	_____	Anderson	_____
Yee	_____	Taylor	_____
Nguyen	_____	Anderson	_____
Blum	_____	Anderson	_____

Name:

Track-and-Field 2

Record the points and missing information on the score sheets.

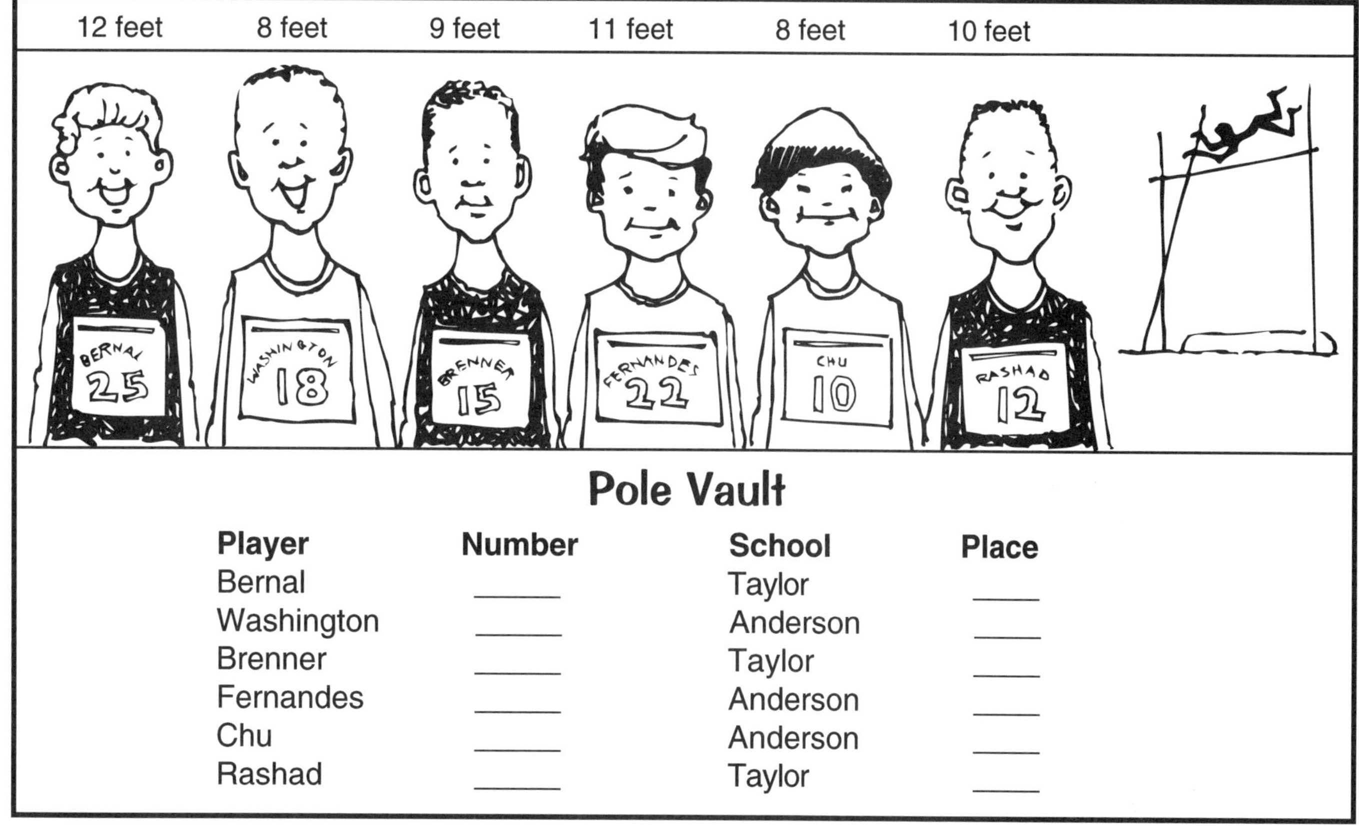

Pole Vault

Player	Number	School	Place
Bernal	______	Taylor	_____
Washington	______	Anderson	_____
Brenner	______	Taylor	_____
Fernandes	______	Anderson	_____
Chu	______	Anderson	_____
Rashad	______	Taylor	_____

51 feet | 48 feet | 39 feet | 49 feet | 40 feet | 46 feet

YEE 19 | ACKERMAN 11 | BUCKNER 46 | NGUYEN 20 | SMITH 28 | MARTIN 15

Shot Put

Player	Number	School	Place
Yee	______	______________	_____
Ackerman	______	______________	_____
Buckner	______	______________	_____
Nguyen	______	______________	_____
Smith	______	______________	_____
Martin	______	______________	_____

Name:

Track-and-Field 3

In this meet, schools gained points for first, second, and third place finishes. Record the points gained in the boxes below.

- First place earns **5 points.**
- Second place earns **3 points.**
- Third place earns **1 point.**
- The other athletes in the event earn no points.
- Tally the wins and points for each school.

Anderson High School

1st place wins	1st place points
2nd place wins	**2nd place points**
3rd place wins	**3rd place points**
	Total points

Taylor High School

1st place wins	1st place points
2nd place wins	**2nd place points**
3rd place wins	**3rd place points**
	Total points

1. Who won the track meet? By how many points?

____

2. Which athletes competed in more than one event? List their names after the name of their school.

Anderson ______________________________

Taylor ______________________________

3. Which athlete earned the most points? ______________________________

How many points? ______________

4. Which event would you like to compete in? ______________________________

Why? ______________________________

Name:

Pinwheel

Follow the steps below to make an interesting wind machine.

Materials
- construction paper 6" x 6" (15 cm) square
- new pencil with eraser
- pushpin
- ruler
- crayons or markers
- tape

Directions

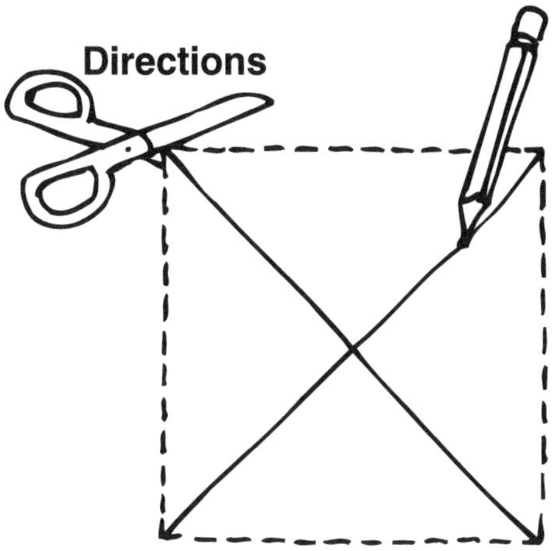

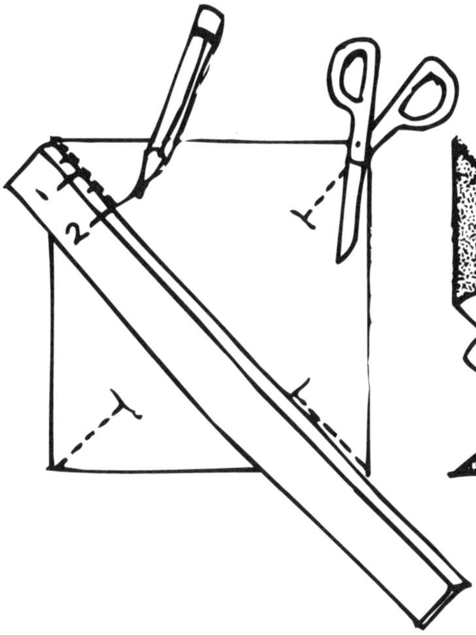

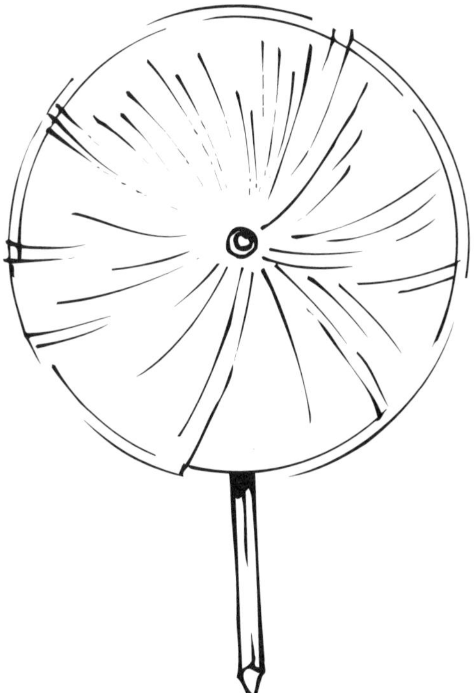

Following Directions

Students need a lot of practice reading and following directions. This section provides four practice activities.

ACTIVITIES

In-line Skates (Pages 11–13)
This activity gives students practice in ordering from a catalog. Depending on the ability level of your students, the pages may be reproduced for independent practice or made into overhead transparencies to use with the whole class.

Put It Together (Pages 14–17)
Students sequence the directions for putting together a bookcase. Make an overhead transparency of page 14 to introduce the lesson. Reproduce pages 15–17 for individual students.

Just for Fun (Pages 18 and 19)
Number and word-puzzle books require careful reading of directions. This activity gives instructions for uncovering a Chinese proverb.

Knot Work (Page 20)
Students match pictures with written directions, learning how to tie a sheet bend knot.

In-line Skates

There are many ways to shop. Some stores send out catalogs so you can shop at home. When you order from a catalog, it's important to read carefully and think about the following things:

- Is the product what you really want to buy?
- Does the quality of the product ensure that it will last a long time?
- Is it the right size?
- Is the price less than the same item in the store, including the shipping and handling charges?

It is time to go shopping with a friend! On these three pages you will help "a friend" order skates and then evaluate his order.

Jeffrey A. O'Brien lives with his parents in Oakville, California (Zip Code 97655). He has been saving money to buy in-line skates. His parents said he had to wait until he had enough money for a helmet and protective pads too. This will ensure his safety as he's skating near his house at 44 Washington Avenue. This month he received $40 for his birthday. Now, with the money he has saved, he has $139.00. He thinks it's enough for medium-priced skates. His shoe size is 7 1/2. He has called you to come over and help him fill out the order form. You telephoned him back at (523) 787-3344 to say you would be right there.

Jeffrey decided to order the following items:

Safe-Landing Protective Pack

#L69398
One size, adjustable 6-piece set.
Knee, elbow, and wrist pads.
Foam inner lining with hard plastic outside covers for the knees and elbows.
Weight: 2.20 lbs.

Price $18.69

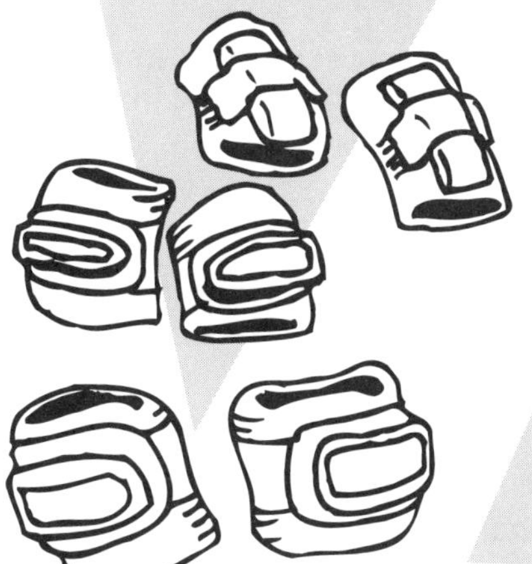

Dial-a-Size Helmet

#M89356
Adjustable. Fits most adults.
Red, blue, or silver.
Safety helmet suitable for most sports except motorcycling. Air vents.
Weight: 2.80 lbs.

Price $41.20

Lightning In-line Skates

#C97321
One-piece construction. Vented polyurethane boot with comfort insoles. Y class bearings and medium-hard wheels. Long-lasting, with a feel for the road.
Adult sizes 6, 7, 8, 9, 10, 11, 12.
6-piece protective pack included.
Rink safe. Weight: 8 lbs.

Price: $51.98

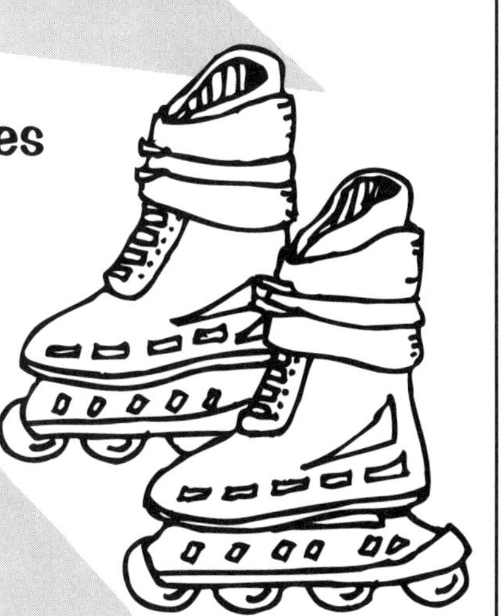

Name:

In-line Skates 2

Fill in the following order form. Be careful to read and follow all the directions.

Best Buy Catalog

Name: First   Middle Initial   Last   Area Code   Telephone

Address   City   State   Zip Code

Item	Catalog Number	Weight	Size	Color	Price
1					
2					
3					
4					

Total price of order:________________

Sales tax (8%):________________

Total weight: ________ Shipping and handling:________________

Amount owed:________________

Ordering Information

Women and girls should order skates two sizes smaller than their regular shoe size. Skates are not available in half sizes. Order the next higher size if you need a half size. Enclose a check or money order that includes the shipping and handling charges and sales tax for your state.

Refunds

If you are not satisfied with your purchase, you may return the order. Merchandise must be returned within thirty days after receipt. Postage, shipping and handling charges, and sales tax will be refunded if the merchandise has not been damaged by the customer. If you are due a refund, a separate check will be mailed to you within thirty days after the store receives the returned merchandise.

Shipping Charges

Weight	Delivery Charges
0–4.9 lbs.	$6.00
5–9.9 lbs.	$8.00
10–19.9 lbs.	$12.50
20–34.9 lbs.	$15.00

For each additional pound, add 25¢. Weights are listed by tenths of a pound. Total the weight for the entire order before adding the shipping and handling charges.

Name:

In-line Skates 3

After filling out the catalog order form, answer the following questions about Jeffrey's order.

1. Why will Jeffrey be surprised when he receives his order?

____

____

____

2. What can Jeffrey do to correct the mistake he made? Read the section on **Refunds** before you write your answer.

____

____

____

3. What is the amount of the refund Jeffrey will receive? Don't forget to include any extra money he paid for shipping and handling, sales tax, and $3.69 he paid for postage to return the merchandise. Show all your work here.

4. How long will Jeffrey need to wait for his refund?

____

5. What could Jeffrey have done differently so that he would not have to go to the trouble of returning something?

____

6. Have you ever ordered anything from a catalog? ______________

   If yes, what was the last thing you ordered? ______________

Put It Together

Many items bought in the store have to be assembled, or put together, when you bring them home. The first step in assembling a bookcase, tool, or toy is to read the directions and then make sure all the parts listed are in the package. Next, see what tools you will need to put the item together. Set up a toolbox. Put all the tools you will need in the box.

Margaret loves to read! She bought a new bookcase for her room. It was unassembled. Complete sheet 2, then follow the instructions on sheets 3 and 4 to help Margaret assemble her bookcase.

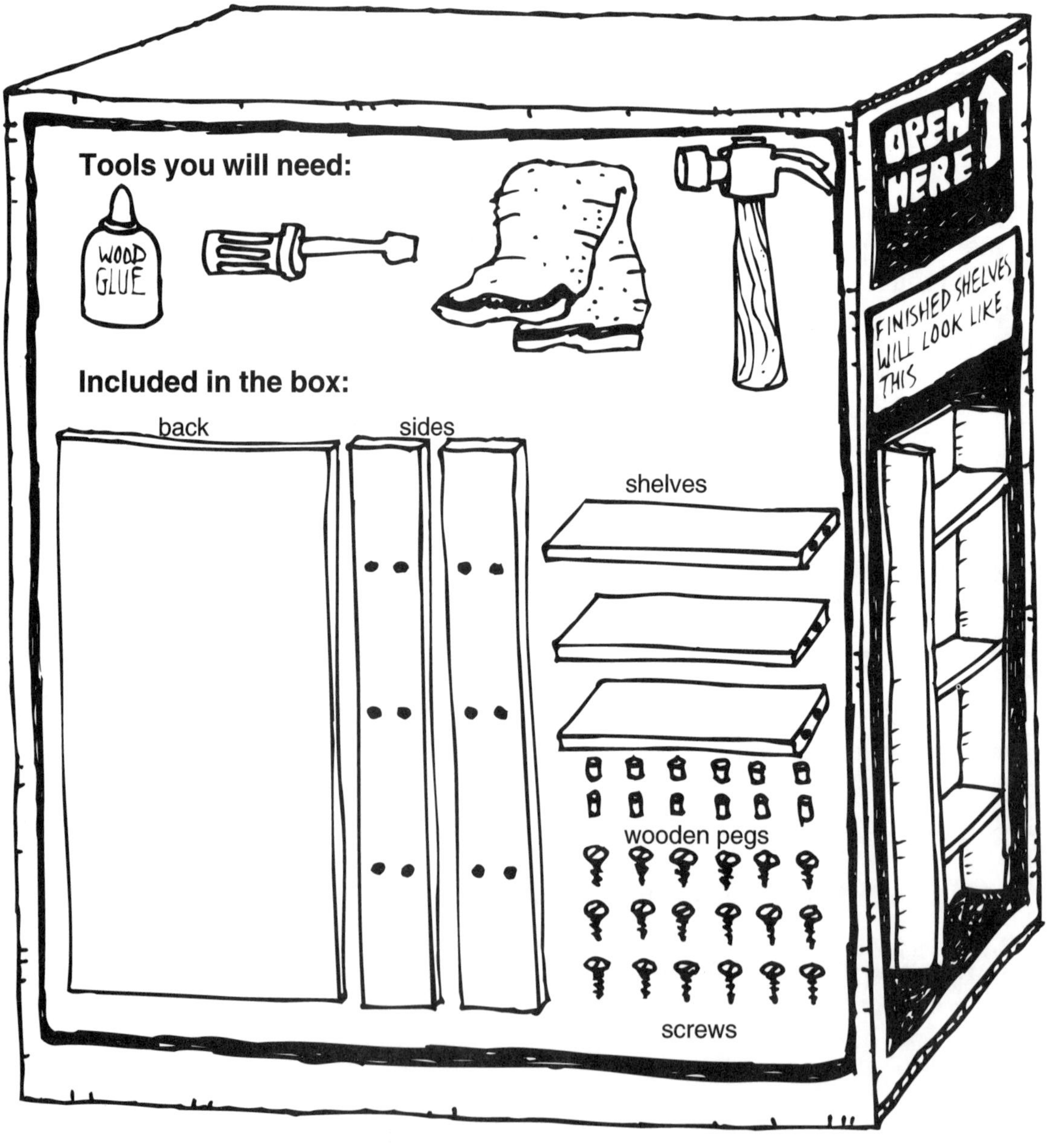

Tools you will need:

WOOD GLUE

Included in the box:

back

sides

shelves

wooden pegs

screws

OPEN HERE

FINISHED SHELVES WILL LOOK LIKE THIS

Name:

Put It Together 2

1. List four steps Margaret should follow before she begins to put the bookcase together:

   First ______________________________

   Then ______________________________

   Next ______________________________

   Then ______________________________

2. List the tools needed to put the bookcase together:

   ______________________ ______________________

   ______________________ ______________________

3. List all the parts and how many of each are included for building the bookcase.

Number	Name
__________	______________
__________	______________
__________	______________
__________	______________
__________	______________

4. Draw a picture in the box of what you think the bookcase will look like after it is assembled and Margaret has filled it.

Name:

Put It Together 3

Let's follow the steps that Margaret followed to build her bookcase.

Read the directions carefully for assembling the bookcase. Cut out the pictures on page 17 and paste each illustration in the box next to the correct step.

Margaret Builds a Bookcase

1. Flatten the cardboard box that the bookcase came in and use it to cover the floor where you are working. It will keep glue off the floor.	paste here
2. Begin with the bottom shelf and the left side of the bookcase. Set the boards flat on the cardboard. Fill the holes on one end of the shelf with glue. Fill the two holes at the bottom of the side board with glue.	paste here
3. Place two pegs in the two glued holes on the side board. Fasten the other ends of the pegs to the glued holes in the shelf. With the hammer, gently tap the top edge of the shelf until the pegs are tightly locked into the side board. There should be no space between the two boards. Wipe off the excess glue.	paste here
4. Fasten the other two shelves in the same way.	paste here
5. When all three shelves are tight and the glue is set, fill all the holes on the open side of the shelves with glue. Fill the holes in the right side board with glue. Place one end of the pegs in the holes in the three shelves. Line up the holes on the right side of the board that is facing up with the shelf pegs and insert the pegs in the holes.	paste here

6. Carefully set a towel over the side board. Gently pound the side board, moving from one peg to another, until there is no space between the shelves and the side boards.

paste here

7. When the glue is set, place the bookcase facedown on the cardboard. Put the two top corner screws into the pre-drilled holes in the bookcase back. Be sure they are lined up with the holes in the bookcase side board. Tighten the screws. Fasten the bottom screws next.

paste here

8. Attach the remaining screws for a sturdy bookcase.

paste here

Name:

Just for Fun

Following directions will help you solve many picture and word puzzles. Complete the instructions below to fill in the letters for this wise Chinese proverb.

. .   . . —   . .   .

___ ___   ___ ___ ___   ___ ___ ___ ___   ___ ___   ___ ___ ___ ___
1 2   3 4 5   6 7 8 9   10 11   12 13 14 15

. —   . . —   . —   . .   . —

___   ___ ___ ___ ___ ___ ___ ___ ___,   ___ ___ ___ ___ ___
16   17 18 19 20 21 22 23 24,   25 26 27 28 29

. —   . —   . —   .   .

___ ___ ___ ___   ___   ___ ___ ___   ___ ___ ___ ___ ___ ___
30 31 32 33   34   35 36 37   38 39 40 41 42 43

. —   . —

___ ___   ___   ___ ___ ___ ___.
44 45   46   47 48 49 50.

1. The last word in this saying is a word that describes seconds, minutes, and hours.
2. There are four more "T's" in this saying. Write the letter "T" above the following numbers: 10, 21, 39, 45.
3. There are 5 "O's" in this saying. "O" is the second letter in words two, four, five, and seven. It is the third letter in the fourth word from the end.
4. Morse code is a system of dots and dashes that represent letters.

   Use the code to fill in the vowels in the proverb.

5. There are three "Y's" in this proverb. The first one is the first letter of the second word. The other two are at the end of the eighth and ninth words.
6. Write the letter "W" over numbers 6, 31, and 37.
7. The first letter of the fifth and seventh words is the third letter of the last word in the proverb.

Name:

Just for Fun 2

8. There are two “R’s” next to each other in the eighth word.
9. The third word rhymes with “fish.”
10. The eleventh word means “not many.”
11. The twelfth word begins and ends with “S.”
12. The eighth word means “to transport something.”
13. Three “N’s”, one “F”, one “V”, and one “C” are missing. Write them in the correct spaces.

You’ve solved the puzzle! In your own words, write what the proverb means.

“Rome wasn’t built in a day” is another well-known saying that is similar to the mystery proverb. How are the two proverbs alike?

Challenge
Work in pairs to write mystery messages. Make up a code. See if your classmates can follow your directions and discover the message.

Name:

Knot Work

Directions can help someone build a house, operate a car, or fix a television set. You can learn to make things by reading the directions in hobby and craft books. The following directions will show you how to tie a special kind of knot.

Write the letter of each picture in the box next to the matching directions.

☐ **1.** The sheet bend knots two pieces of rope together. It is a good knot to use when you need to tie ropes that are not the same thickness.

☐ **2.** Hold one of the ropes with one hand. Wrap the free end of the rope around the hand holding the rope.

☐ **3.** Slip your fingers out of the rope. Set the loop on a flat surface. The loose end of the string that goes to the right must be on the underneath side of the loop.

☐ **4.** Pick up the other piece of rope with the other hand. Pull one end of the rope under the bottom of the loop and out over the top of the loop.

☐ **5.** The end of this rope goes underneath the right end of the other rope above the loop.

☐ **6.** Bring the rope you pulled through the loop back down through the loop—a U-turn.

☐ **7.** Pull on both ends of the U-turn rope and both top ends of the other rope to tie the knot.

A B C D E F G

Now try to tie a sheet bend knot. Books on knot tying are available. Practice tying a variety of knots. Amaze your friends and family.

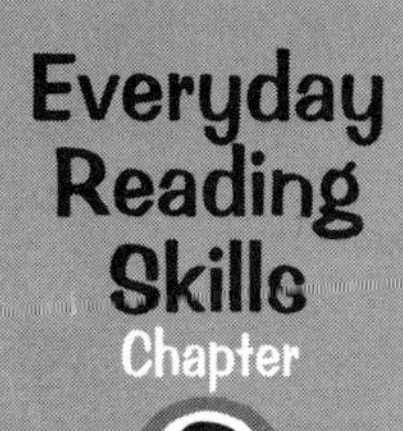

Finding Names and Numbers

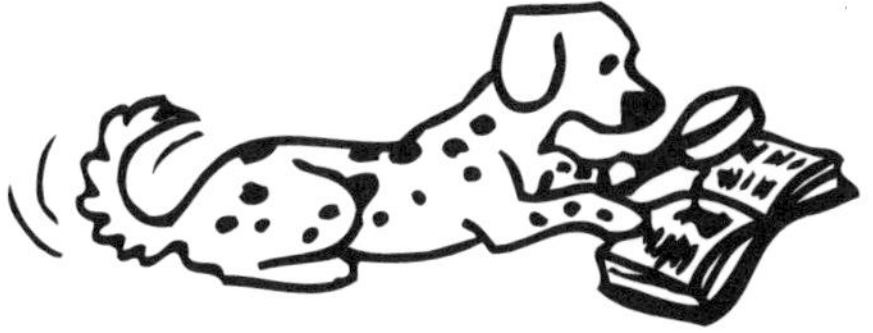

We read to find addresses and telephone numbers of businesses and individuals so we can call, write letters, shop, visit, send cards, and so on.

Introduce the activities in this section by asking students to explain how a telephone book is organized to help us find information. Divide the class into small groups. Give each group a copy of a telephone book. After students have looked through their books, discuss the different types of information telephone books contain.

ACTIVITIES

What's in a Telephone Book? (Pages 22 and 23)
Use a model of a telephone book white page to practice finding information in a telephone book. Make a transparency or reproduce page 22 for each student. Page 23 contains questions that may be asked orally or reproduced to use as a written activity.

Find It in the Yellow Pages (Pages 24 and 25)
Use a model of a telephone book yellow page to practice finding information in a telephone book. Make a transparency or reproduce the page for each student. Page 25 contains questions that may be asked orally or reproduced to use as a written activity.

For additional practice, laminate pages from an old telephone book and make a task card to fit each page. Place the cards in a center. Have students work in pairs or independently to find the answers.

Using an Address Book (Page 26)
Reproduce this page on a transparency or make a copy for each student. Ask questions about the names, addresses, and telephone numbers on the page.

Provide construction paper and lined paper for students to use to create their own address books.

The Telephone Book

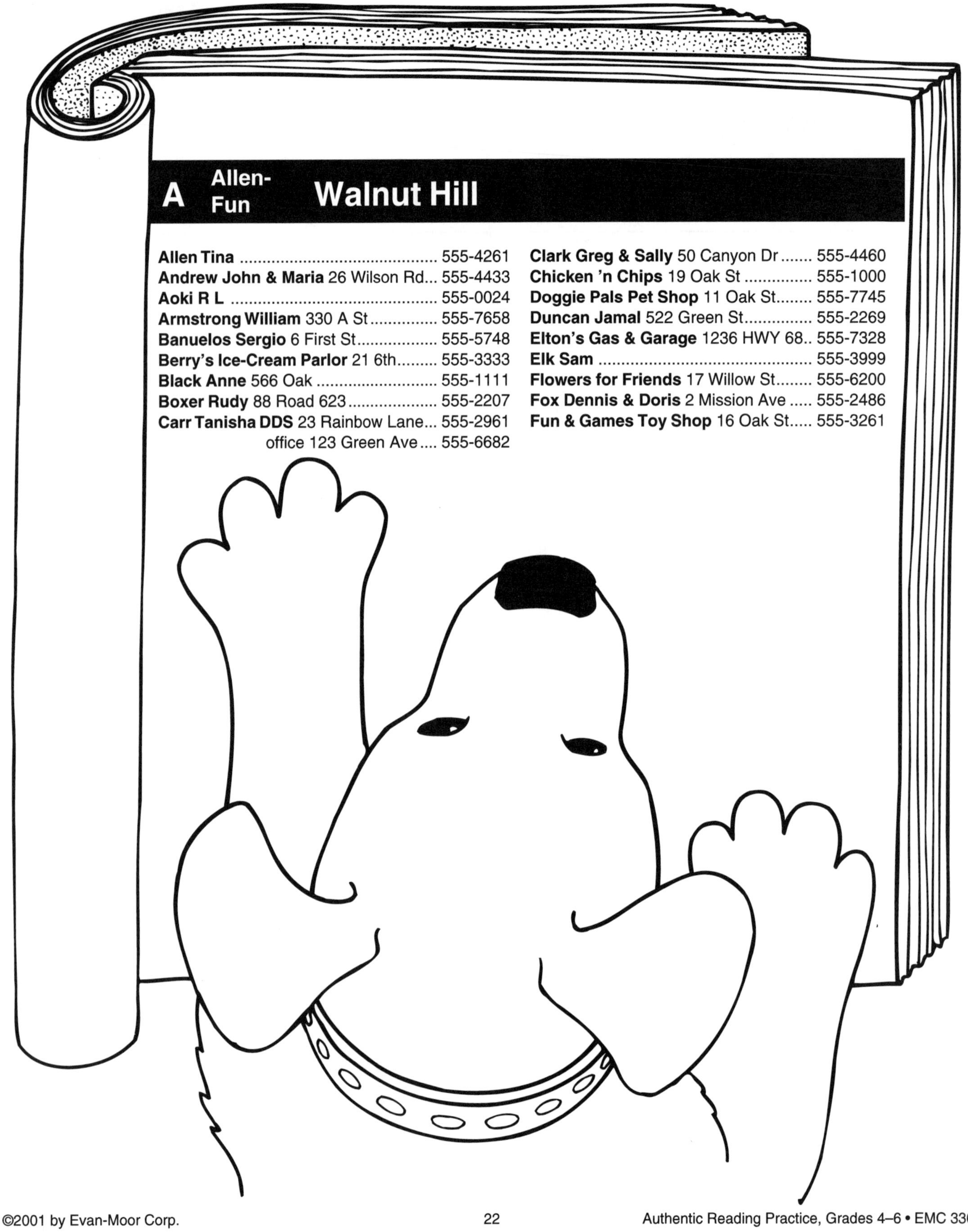

A Allen-Fun Walnut Hill

Allen Tina 555-4261
Andrew John & Maria 26 Wilson Rd... 555-4433
Aoki R L 555-0024
Armstrong William 330 A St.............. 555-7658
Banuelos Sergio 6 First St.................. 555-5748
Berry's Ice-Cream Parlor 21 6th......... 555-3333
Black Anne 566 Oak 555-1111
Boxer Rudy 88 Road 623.................... 555-2207
Carr Tanisha DDS 23 Rainbow Lane... 555-2961
office 123 Green Ave.... 555-6682
Clark Greg & Sally 50 Canyon Dr....... 555-4460
Chicken 'n Chips 19 Oak St 555-1000
Doggie Pals Pet Shop 11 Oak St........ 555-7745
Duncan Jamal 522 Green St............... 555-2269
Elton's Gas & Garage 1236 HWY 68.. 555-7328
Elk Sam 555-3999
Flowers for Friends 17 Willow St........ 555-6200
Fox Dennis & Doris 2 Mission Ave 555-2486
Fun & Games Toy Shop 16 Oak St..... 555-3261

Finding Names & Numbers

Name:

What's in a Telephone Book?

1. What is the first name you read on this page? What is her telephone number?

___

2. Where does Anne Black live? What is her telephone number?

___

3. How many people with a last name beginning with A are on this page?

___

4. What street is the dentist's office on?

___

5. What is Mr. Elk's first name?

___

6. What three businesses are on Oak Street?

___

___

___

7. Where would you go if you wanted to buy ice cream?

___

8. What number would you call if you wanted to order flowers for someone's birthday?

___

The Yellow Pages

Pets

Park Place Wash-a-Pet
Do-It-Yourself Pet Wash
7 days a week

662 Park Place.......555-6328

Pat's Pet Center

661 First St 555-3379

Pet Place

at Mission Mall
Discount Pet
Super Store

- low prices on pet food
- fish and aquariums
- rats, guinea pigs, hamsters
- reptiles
- do-it-yourself pet wash
- pet grooming

555-8731 • Next to the Bargain Barn

Tropical Fish & Birds

- Over 11,000 Tropical Fish in Stock
- Aquariums & Aquarium Supplies
- We install in your home or business

- All Kinds of Birds
- Complete Line of Bird Feeders
- Cages & Supplies

Expert advice on fish & bird care
Open 7 days a week
555-0102
1335 Willow Street, Walnut Hill

PABLO'S PETS

Since 1976
42 6th Street
555-5531

Pet Grooming
Pet Supplies

Perfect Pet Food

31 Green Ave 555-3620

Humane Society of Walnut Hill

11-5 M-F

11-1 Sat, Sun

555-4472 1339 HWY 68

WE CARE

Pet Shop

• Expert Advice • Pet Grooming • Pet Supplies

555-5571
M-F 8-6 Sat 9-5

49 Elm Street (behind the Post Office)

Name:

Find It in the Yellow Pages

1. What kind of shops are listed on this page?

____

2. What different kinds of information can you learn by reading this page?

____

____

____

3. What is the telephone number of WE CARE Pet Shop?

____

4. What can you buy at Pablo's Pets?

____

5. What hours is the Humane Society open?

____

6. Which shop would you call to ask a question about a tropical bird?

____

7. On what street is Pat's Pet Center located?

____

8. You want to give your dog a bath yourself. Where can you go?

____

Name:

Using an Address Book

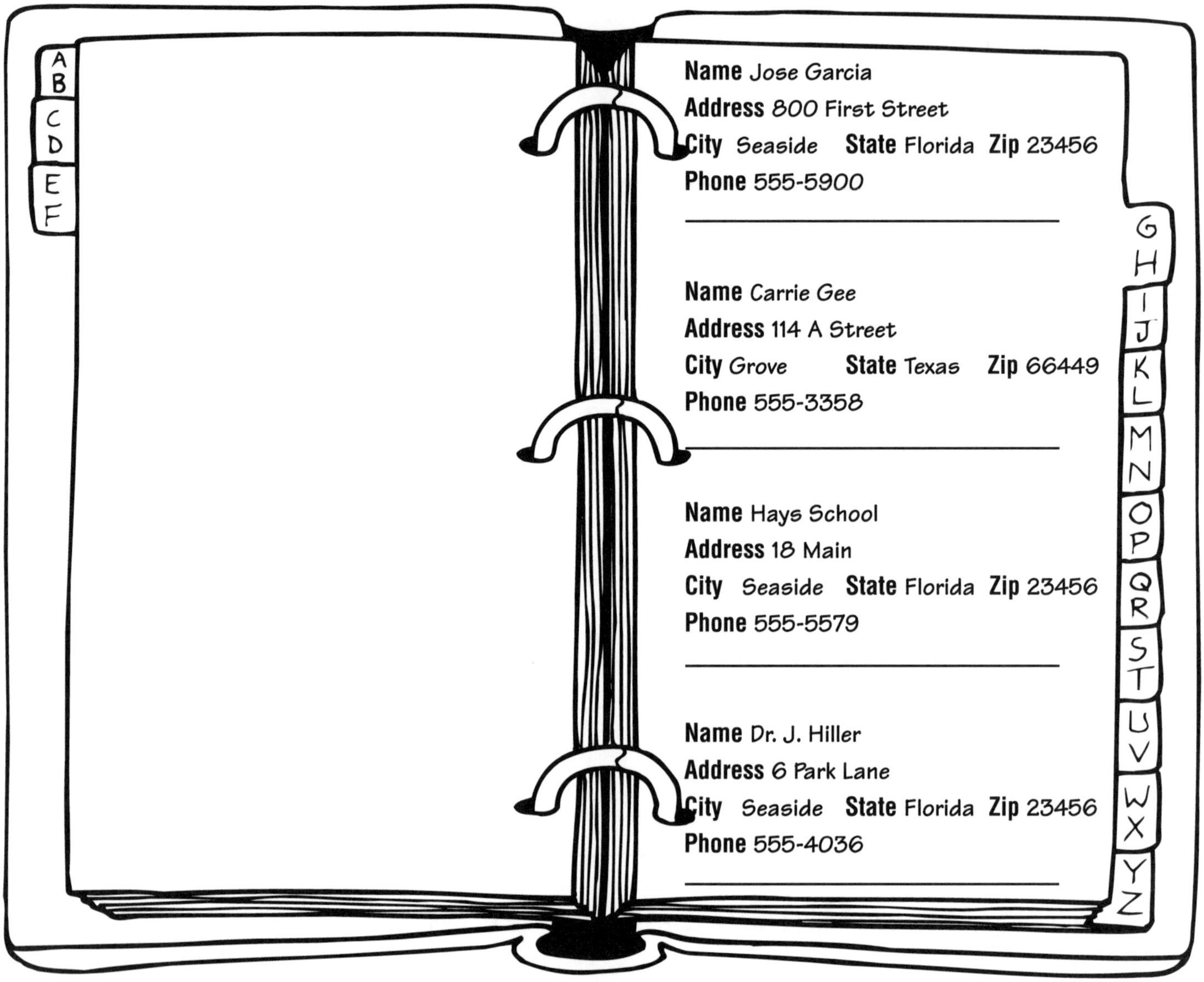

A B
C D
E F

Name Jose Garcia
Address 800 First Street
City Seaside **State** Florida **Zip** 23456
Phone 555-5900

Name Carrie Gee
Address 114 A Street
City Grove **State** Texas **Zip** 66449
Phone 555-3358

Name Hays School
Address 18 Main
City Seaside **State** Florida **Zip** 23456
Phone 555-5579

Name Dr. J. Hiller
Address 6 Park Lane
City Seaside **State** Florida **Zip** 23456
Phone 555-4036

G H
I J
K L
M N
O P
Q R
S T
U V
W X
Y Z

Write your name, address, and telephone number here:

Name ______________________________

Address ______________________________

____

City ______________ State ________ Zip ________

Phone ______________________________

Forms and Applications

When you want to go to camp, enter a drawing to win a prize, apply for a job, or get a library card, you need to read directions and fill out forms and applications. In this section, students will practice these necessary life skills. Be sure to introduce vocabulary that your students may not know.

ACTIVITIES

Working in the School Store (Pages 28–30)

Students fill out an application and then answer questions to show that they understand the content of the application form. They then write a letter stating why they wish to have the job. The letter model may be reproduced for students or made into a transparency.

Camp Goodtimes (Pages 31–33)

Pages 31 and 32 contain a mock summer camp application form. Before beginning this activity, decide if you will actually send home the forms to obtain parent signatures and emergency information. Discuss the fact that students are minors, what that means, and why a parent or guardian's signature is required. Page 33 contains questions that assess student understanding of the camp application form.

Applying for a Job (Pages 34 and 35)

Page 34 models a completed job application. Use page 35 to assess how accurately the application was filled out. Discuss what a Social Security number is and why it is needed. You might want to obtain forms from your local Social Security office and fill them out as a class activity.

Applying for a Library Card (Page 36)

Fill out a card application form for a fictional library. If you have a nearby local library, fill out the real thing.

Name:

Working in the School Store

You have decided to apply to work during lunchtime in the school store. You need to fill out the application and write a letter explaining why you want to work in the store.

Application to Work in the School Store

Name ____

Grade ____________________ Room Number _______________

Teacher's Name ____

Circle days you are able to work: M T W TH F

1. I will be willing to work as a substitute in the store when other helpers are absent.
Yes **No**

2. My citizenship grade was satisfactory for the past two months of school.
Yes **No**

3. I received passing grades for all my subjects on the last report card.
Yes **No**

If your teacher signs this application, you may apply to work in the store even if the answer to the last question is No.

___________________________ has my permission to work in the school store.

____
(Teacher's Signature)

- If selected to work in the store for three months, I will leave my classroom twenty minutes early to eat my lunch on the one day I am working.
- I will report for work on time.
- I will return to class twenty minutes after the store closes.
- I will be respectful to customers and other workers in the store.
- I will do my best to follow directions and complete my duties.
- I will help put away the merchandise and fill out the records for the sales and money received that day.
- I understand I need to make up any work I miss when I am not in my classroom.

Your Signature: ______________________________________

Name:

Working in the School Store 2

Answer the following questions about the application.

1. How long will each person work in the store?

____

2. How many days a week will each person work?

____

3. What will happen if someone is absent?

____

4. What duties will students have while working in the store?

____

____

____

____

____

5. How much classroom time will each student worker miss each week?

____

6. In what ways can a store worker be respectful to customers? _______________

____

7. Joe buys 3 pencils that cost 25¢ each, a book cover that costs 75¢, 2 erasers that cost 30¢ each, and an apple that costs 50¢. How much change will you give him back from the $5.00 bill he gave you? Show all your work below.

Name:

Working in the School Store 3

Write a letter explaining why you want to work in the school store.

This is a guide for how to write a business letter:

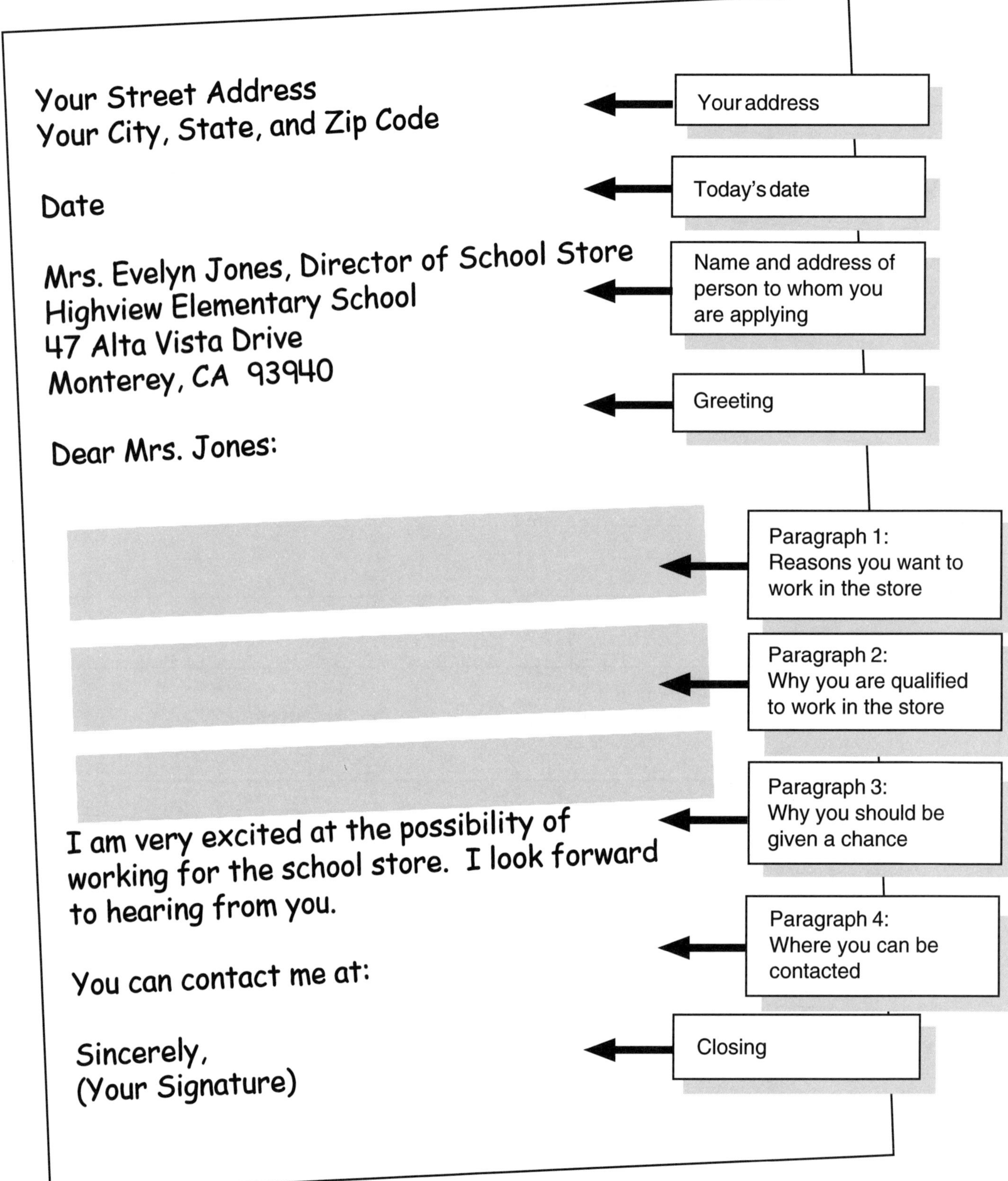

Camp Goodtimes

Section 1 - Personal Information

First Name Middle Initial Last Name

Address City State Zip Code

Telephone

Date of Birth Grade School

Circle: Male Female

Session You Wish to Attend:

July 5 - July 19 July 21 - August 6 August 8 - August 22

Major Activity:

Sports and Swimming Computers Art and Music

Note: Campers will have many outdoor activities in addition to the section they have chosen.

Section 2 - Emergency Information

1. List any activities the camper cannot participate in ____________________

2. List allergies, physical limitations ____________________

3. List any medications the camper needs to take ____________________

4. Parent/Guardian's Name ____________________

____
Address City State Zip Code

5. Work Telephone ____________________

6. Home Telephone ____________________

7. Emergency Contacts
List two people the camp can contact if the parent/guardian is not available.

A. Name ____________________
Telephone ____________________
Relationship ____________________

B. Name ____________________
Telephone ____________________
Relationship ____________________

8. Persons who may pick up the camper beside the parent:

____

Anyone picking up the child at camp must be listed on this application. Picture identification is required. Please notify the camp director if the camper will be going home with someone other than the parent.

Parent or Guardian's Signature ____________________ Date ____________________

This application must be mailed by May 1.

Name:

Camp Goodtimes 3

Answer the following questions about the application.

1. List three safety procedures the camp has to protect the campers.

____

____

____

2. Why does the application have questions about health and medication?

____

3. Who must sign the application?

____

4. By what date should the application be mailed?

____

Applying for a Job

Martin Palma will celebrate his eighteenth birthday on the first day of July. He graduates from Oneida City High School on June 15. Martin needs to earn money to help pay for college expenses in the fall. Last summer he worked mowing and trimming lawns. This summer he wants to work full-time at Baker's Food Market. He filled out the application on April 3. Martin wants to begin work the week after he graduates. He would like to be a check-out clerk, bag groceries, stock shelves, or help in the fresh produce department. Since the college he will go to is nearby, he plans to work one day on the weekends during the school year. Read Martin's job application carefully. Sheet 2 will ask you questions about it.

Baker's Food Market

1. Print full name: Martin (Last Name) Antonio (First Name) Palma (Middle Name)

2. Address: 294 Park Avenue (Number and Street) Oneida (City) (State) 42765 (Zip Code)

3. 443-2214 (Telephone Number) 739-27-6661 (Social Security Number)

4. Education: Oneida City High School Did you graduate? (Yes) No

   College: Appleton University Are you a student? (Yes) No

5. Work Experience: Any job available

6. For what job are you applying? Gardening, mowing lawns

7. When can you work? (Circle the times below.)
   - (Full-time)
   - (Part-time)
   - (After school)
   - (Weekends)

8. When can you begin work? June 22

If you are under 18 years of age, you must attach a work permit. Check here if attached. ☐

Name:

Applying for a Job 2

Martin made errors when he filled out the application.

Go over the application carefully and circle as many mistakes as you can find. List them here:

1. ____________________

2. ____________________

3. ____________________

4. ____________________

5. ____________________

6. ____________________

7. ____________________

Answer the following questions about the application.

1. Because Martin was almost 18 years old, he did not attach a work permit, but he should have. When could he start work without the permit?

____

2. How should Martin write his name on the application form?

____

3. Write your name in the same order.

____

4. Martin wants full-time summer work and part-time work during the following school year. Since there wasn't room to explain on the form, Martin needs to write an explanation. On the lines below, write the explanation for Martin.

____

____

____

____

Name:

Applying for a Library Card

When applying for a library card, you will need a parent or guardian's signature and proof that your family lives in the city served by the library. A rent receipt, a driver's license, or an electric bill are some of the items that could be used to prove where your family lives.

Fill out the following application for a library card.

Jackson County Library

Please Print

Name ____

(Last) (First) (Middle Initial)

Mailing Address

____

(Street Address or P.O. Box)

____

(City) (State) (Zip Code)

Home Address if Different from Mailing Address

____

(Address) (City) (State) (Zip Code)

If you have moved during the last two years, or changed your name, please list your previous address or name below.

Previous Name ____

Previous Address ____

I have had a County Library Card before. (Circle) Yes No

I agree to follow all the library rules. I will pay promptly any library fines for lost or damaged books. I will be responsible for all materials checked out with my card.

____

(Signature)

If you are under age 14, your parent or legal guardian must sign this application.

____

(Signature of Parent or Guardian)

Contests, Rebates, and Advertisements

Contests, product rebates, and advertisements all require careful reading. Lack of comprehension may mean not complying with all the rules, not getting a refund, or buying a product that doesn't fulfill expectations.

Introduce the words *promote, endorse, techniques, persuade,* and *convince.*

ACTIVITIES

The Winning Ticket (Pages 38 and 39)
Students fill out a form to win a prize and then answer questions about the form.

Sending for a Rebate (Page 40)
Students must read carefully to find out how to get money back on a product.

Buy! Buy! Buy! (Pages 41 and 42)
This lesson introduces techniques used by advertisers to convince people to buy a product. Students then evaluate five ads to determine the technique used.

The Winning Ticket

When you fill out forms to win prizes, you need to follow directions carefully. Read the directions to fill out the entry blank on this sheet. Answer the questions about it on sheet 2.

Entry Blank

Win a new bicycle, a computer, or a movie for your home entertainment center! There are hundreds of prizes, including free movie-rental certificates. No purchase necessary. Just fill out this entry blank and deposit it in the entry blank box at *Hazel's Movie Stop*. One entry blank per person. Entry blanks must be deposited by March 1. Winning entry blanks will be drawn on March 2. You do not need to be present to win. To help us serve our customers, answer the three questions at the bottom of the entry blank and turn it in at the counter. You'll receive a certificate for a free candy bar when you rent your next movie.

Hazel's Movie Stop

____
Name

____
Address

____
Telephone Number

Cut here

1. About how many movies do you rent each month? ______________

2. Circle the three types of movies you enjoy the most.

comedies	musicals	cartoons
children's movies	westerns	drama
action		

3. What can *Hazel's* do to improve service to customers?

____

Name:

The Winning Ticket 2

1. By what date must the entry blanks be in the box? ______________________

2. Do you have to be present to win? ______________________

3. What three things do you have to do before you receive the gift?

____

____

____

4. How many prizes will be awarded?

____

5. Rewrite the sentence about the prizes so customers will know the exact number of prizes *Hazel's* will give away. You decide the number.

____

____

6. What will you receive if you fill out the questionnaire at the bottom of the entry blank?

____

Name:

Sending for a Rebate

When you fill out a form to receive a rebate (money back), you need to follow directions carefully. Read the directions for sending for a rebate for *Red-Hot Chewy Fireballs.*

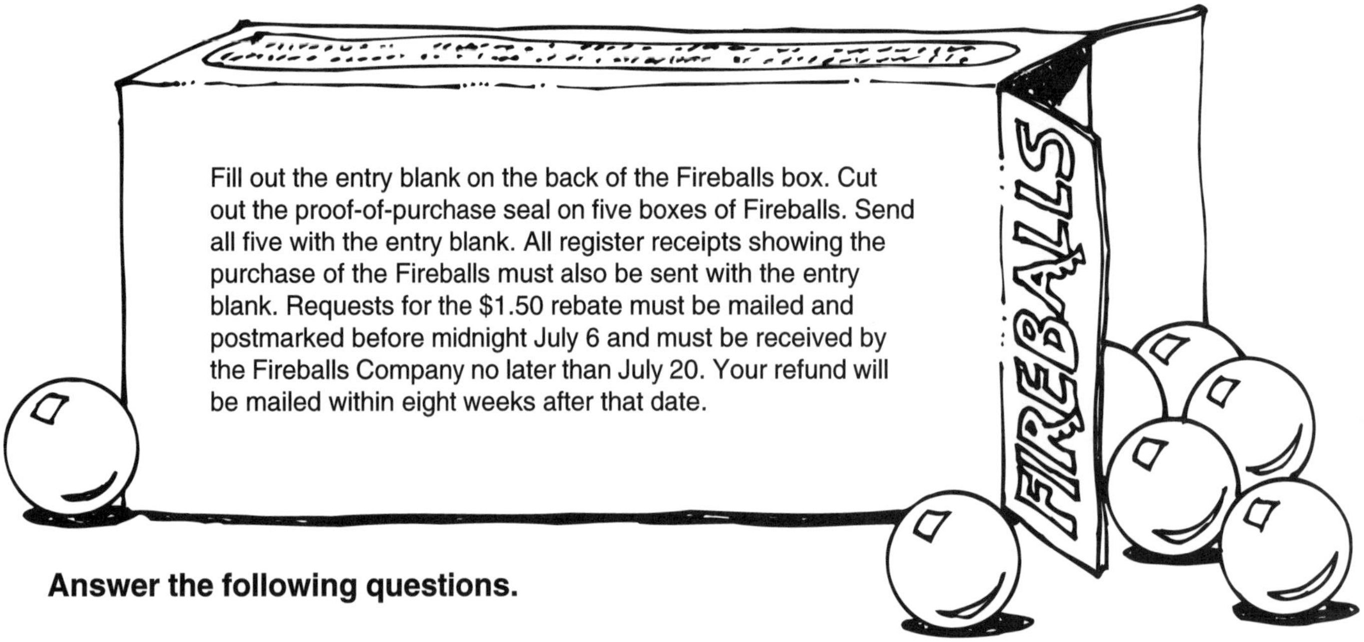

FIREBALLS

Fill out the entry blank on the back of the Fireballs box. Cut out the proof-of-purchase seal on five boxes of Fireballs. Send all five with the entry blank. All register receipts showing the purchase of the Fireballs must also be sent with the entry blank. Requests for the $1.50 rebate must be mailed and postmarked before midnight July 6 and must be received by the Fireballs Company no later than July 20. Your refund will be mailed within eight weeks after that date.

Answer the following questions.

1. List the three things that you must send to receive the rebate.

____

____

____

2. Postage to send for the rebate costs 40¢. Why it is important to consider the cost of postage when sending for rebates?

____

____

____

3. By what date must your request for a rebate be received?

____

4. How long could it take to receive the rebate?

____

Buy! Buy! Buy!

Advertisers use different techniques to try to convince people that they really need a product. Here are five such techniques.

1. **Join the Crowd**
   Some advertisements make you think that large numbers of people use the product. The ads try to convince you to join the crowd and buy it too. They may use percentages and say that 85% or 95% of all the people surveyed use the product. Of course, the advertisement may not let you know who these people are or how often they use the product.

2. **Ask an Expert**
   Experts interviewed in an ad say it's a great product. For example, a doctor says she recommends a headache medicine for her patients. These experts are paid to advertise and endorse (associate their name with) the product. The advertisement doesn't say if they use other products as well.

3. **Be the Best**
   If a famous basketball player says he plays better when he wears Brand X athletic shoes, other people will buy the shoes so they can be better athletes and win more basketball games. Most famous people are paid large amounts of money to advertise a product.

4. **Over and Over Again**
   An advertisement may repeat the brand name many times so people will think of that name when they go to the store. For example, Sudsy Soap TV advertisements show that clothes washed in Sudsy are bright and clean. They repeat the word Sudsy in every sentence. When viewers shop, they'll remember the name Sudsy.

5. **Superb, Marvelous, and Fantastic**
   Some ads use descriptive words and pictures to convince people that the products will improve people's lives or the way they feel. An ad may show a beautiful tropical sunset on an island beach. Words like *unforgettable, breathtaking, peaceful,* and *heavenly* are used with the picture to convince travelers to vacation on the island. Negative words, words that make you uncomfortable, can be used to show that people who don't use a product will be very unhappy. For example, you can have tired, aching feet that make you feel miserable if you don't wear Comfy Slippers while you do your homework.

Name:

Buy! Buy! Buy! 2

Read the following advertisements. Which of the five techniques did the advertisers use to sell the product? Write the number of the technique in the circle at the top left of each advertisement.

FLUFFY

Fluffy is a winner. She has a room filled with trophies and blue ribbons to prove it. She's been named "Top Cat" at cat shows all over the country. To keep her prize-winning form, Fluffy eats top-quality *Super Cat*. The ingredients in *Super Cat* keep Fluffy healthy and content. Feed your cat *Super Cat,* and watch your feline friend develop winning ways like Fluffy.

SAM'S PIZZA!!!

Come to Sam's Pizza for a mouthwatering treat. Only at Sam's Pizza can you sink your teeth into layer after layer of creamy cheeses topped with tomatoes and garden vegetables. Sam's Pizza's Vegetarian Delight is spread over a crunchy Italian crust. Right now Sam's Pizza has a special you won't want to miss—two giant-size pizzas for the price of one! So tonight, let Sam's Pizza cook, set the table, and wash the dishes. Call Sam's Pizza and reserve a table. Sam's Pizza has banquet rooms big enough for the whole family. Bring your cousins, uncles, aunts, and grandparents to Sam's.

SNEAKERS

Sneakers* outsells all other brands of sports shoes. Three out of four people surveyed chose *Sneakers* over other brands. For walking, jogging, aerobics, or tennis, *Sneakers* has the style you need. Be part of the team. Go *Sneakers!

GLOW Toothpaste

Dr. Ana Lee recommends ***Glow Toothpaste***. "***Glow*** keeps me smiling. I recommend it for its fresh mint flavor and its decay-fighting ingredients. There's always a tube of ***Glow*** in my medicine cabinet at home."

Now it's your turn!

Write a list of words about your favorite food that would make other people want to eat that food. Use some of those words to fill in the blanks for the following advertisement.

______________________ "Yummy Bar"

When you bite into a ______________ Yummy Bar, close your eyes and smell the ______________ chocolate coating and cherry caramel filling. Its ______________ aroma will get you ready for Yummy's ______________ taste. Chew slowly and savor each ______________ bite. ______________________________! You deserve a ______________ Yummy break every day.

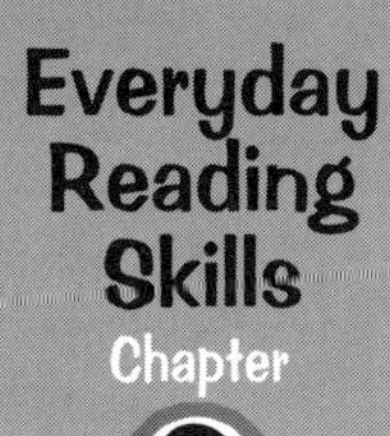

Directions and Diagrams Labels and Signs

In this section students will practice programming a VCR, following directions for a recipe, reading nutritional labels, and locating items in a store.

Before doing "What's for Breakfast?" and "Lunchtime," you may need to provide background information so that students understand nutritional terms (sodium, cholesterol, etc.) and have criteria for determining healthy foods (lower fat, sugar, sodium, cholesterol; high fiber; vitamins and minerals).

ACTIVITIES

Take a Look (Pages 44 and 45)
Students read instructions for operating a VCR and then answer questions to show comprehension of the instructions.

Read to Eat (Page 46)
Students read the recipe for making a delicious soup and then answer questions to show understanding.

What's for Breakfast? (Pages 47 and 48)
Using the nutritional information for two cereals, students answer questions about that information. If desired, assign students to take the form home and fill in the nutritional information for a favorite cereal.

Lunchtime (Pages 49 and 50)
Students use a nutritional guide and a point system to decide which sandwich is the best choice for a fictional character to order.

Aisle Search (Page 51)
Students study the directory of an imaginary store to decide in which aisle various items would be found.

Take a Look

There are many different remote controls for VCRs. It's important to read the directions for any remote control before you turn it on.

Look at the remote control diagram and read the instructions below.

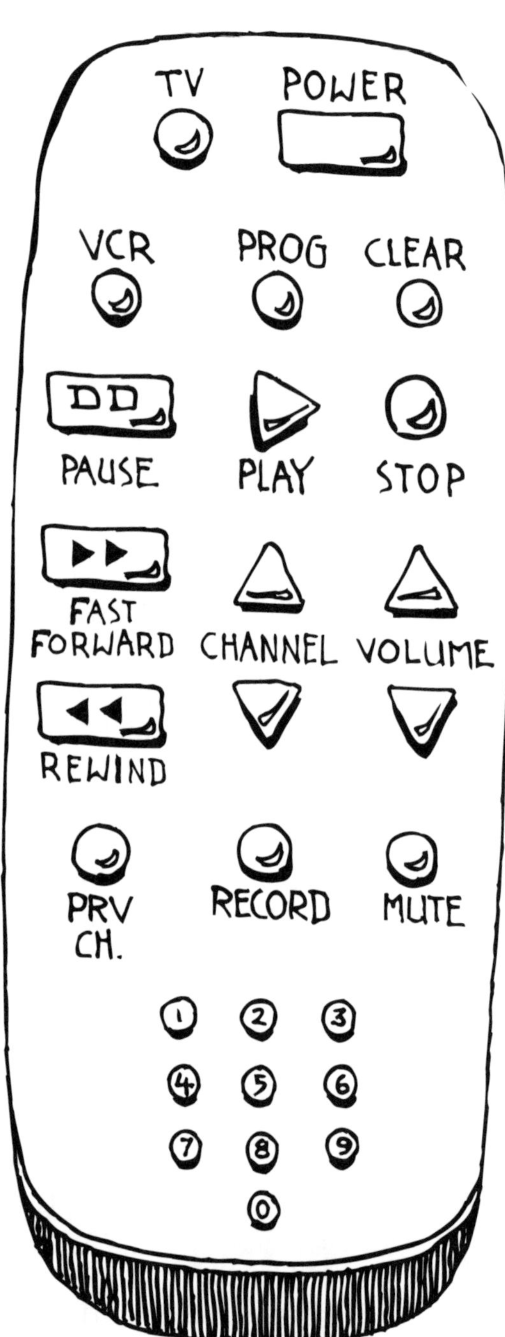

Set the Clock
Press the PROG button. When the program menu comes on, press 3 for clock. Use the numbers on the remote control to set the clock; two for the hour and two for the minutes. For example: for 9:00, punch in 0900. Select AM or PM on the screen. Set the date by pressing six numbers. Always press 0 in front of a one-digit number. Press PROG to activate the clock. To clear a mistake when setting the clock, press CLEAR and begin again.

Record One Program and Watch Another
Put a tape in the VCR. Press the RECORD button. After the recording begins, press the VCR button to turn off the VCR. Select another channel on the TV.

Pause
Use the PAUSE button to interrupt tape recording or playback. To resume recording or playback, press the PAUSE button again.

Channel Switching
Turn on the TV only. Select the first channel. Select a new channel by pressing the number of the second channel. If the channel has only one digit, press 0 first.

Press PRV CH each time you want to change between these two channels.

Mute Button
Press the MUTE button to turn the sound off. Press the MUTE button again to turn the sound back on.

Name:

Take a Look 2

Follow the directions and answer the questions below using page 44.

1. Circle the button that fast-forwards a tape.
2. Underline the button that will begin a recording of a program.
3. Draw an X on the button that immediately turns the sound off.
4. Draw a star on the button that erases programming errors on the clock.
5. If you press PAUSE so a commercial isn't recorded, how do you start recording again?

   ____

6. What numbers do you press to set the VCR clock for 4:30?

   ____

7. After you have set the clock, how do you activate it?

   ____

8. Write four important steps you must follow if you want to watch one program while you record another.

   ❶ ______________________________

   ❷ ______________________________

   ❸ ______________________________

   ❹ ______________________________

Name:

Read to Eat

Reading carefully is extremely important when following a recipe. Imagine what would happen if the recipe called for a tablespoon of salt and you put in a cup! What if the cookies were to bake at 325° and you turned the oven to 425°?

Carefully read this recipe for making delicious minestrone (vegetable) soup.

Delicious Minestrone

1 tablespoon oil
1 clove garlic, minced
1 cup onion, chopped
1 large carrot, sliced into rounds
½ cup uncooked rice
1 teaspoon Italian seasoning
3 cups water
1 10½-ounce can chicken broth
2 14½-ounce cans of chopped tomatoes
2 small or 1 large zucchini, sliced into rounds
¼ teaspoon salt
¼ teaspoon pepper
1 15½-ounce can white beans or kidney beans, drained
1 pound fresh baby spinach leaves
grated parmesan cheese

1. Heat oil in a large pot over medium-high heat.
2. Add garlic, onion, and carrot; cook, stirring for 3 minutes.
3. Add rice and the next 4 ingredients. Bring to a boil.
4. Cover, reduce heat, and simmer 20 minutes.
5. Add zucchini and next 4 ingredients.
6. Cook 5 more minutes.
7. Ladle into bowls and top with parmesan cheese.

Serves 6 to 8.

Now answer the questions about making delicious minestrone.

1. Which four ingredients must be cut up before adding them to the soup?

________________ ________________

________________ ________________

2. Name five different types of vegetables in this soup.

____

3. Step 3 says to add rice and the next 4 ingredients. What are those ingredients?

________________ ________________

________________ ________________

4. What is the total cooking time?

____

5. Does the recipe use more chicken broth or more water?

____

Name:

What's for Breakfast?

It's important to read the labels on the food you buy. Your favorite cereal may do somersaults when you pour on the milk, but it may not provide the nutrition you need.

The ingredients for two different cereals are shown below. Read the information and answer the questions about the two products on sheet 2.

Ingredient	Cereal A	Cereal B	Your Cereal
Calories	150	110	________
Fat	1 gram	2 grams	________
Cholesterol	0	0	________
Sodium	140 mg	110 mg	________
Carbohydrates	24 g	30 g	________
Fiber	3 g	1 g	________
Sugar	10 g	14 g	________
Protein	3 g	3 g	________

Percentage of Daily Food Values for a 2,000-Calorie-a-Day Diet

	Cereal A	Cereal B	Your Cereal
Vitamin A	25	35	________
Vitamin D	25	12	________
Vitamin C	25	25	________
Vitamin B_6	100	20	________
Vitamin B_{12}	25	25	________
Vitamin E	25	25	________
Calcium	25	0	________
Iron	100	25	________
Potassium	2	0	________
Copper	14	14	________
Zinc	4	15	________
Magnesium	100	20	________
Phosphorus	15	15	________
Riboflavin	15	20	________
Folic Acid	25	10	________
Thiamin	25	25	________
Niacin	100	25	________

Name:

What's for Breakfast? 2

1. Compare the two nutrition charts. in the percentage of Daily Food Values columns, which cereal has the greater number of high percentages?

____

2. Some nutrients in Cereal B have a higher percentage than the same nutrients in Cereal A. List them.

_______ _______ _______

3. Which nutrients have the same percentage in both cereals?

_______ _______ _______

_______ _______ _______

4. Cereal A supplies 100 percent of several nutrients. Name them.

_______ _______

_______ _______

5. Cereal B has 0 percent of two nutrients. Name them.

_______ _______

6. Which cereal do you think provides the best nutrition? _______
Give at least three reasons for your choice.

____

____

____

Homework

In the third column on the chart, fill in the information for a breakfast cereal from home. How does your cereal compare with the other two?

____

____

Lunchtime

On Saturday mornings, Nat runs errands for his mother and grandmother. He mows their lawns and does yard work for them. When it's 12:30, he stops for lunch. He spends some of the money he earns for lunch at the Snack Shack. Because he wants to try out for the swim team in the spring, he knows it's important to eat healthy foods.

On the back of the Snack Shack menu is a nutrition guide for the foods served in the restaurant. Nat reads about the sandwiches before he places his order.

Snack Shack

Hot Dogs | Hamburgers | Fries

						% DR			
	Calories	g Fat	mg Cholesterol	mg Sodium	g Protein	Vitamin A	Vitamin C	Calcium	Iron
Super Cheeseburger	510	29	90	1100	28	10	4	15	25
Deluxe Cheeseburger	390	16	65	1040	24	9	12	12	25
Fish Sandwich	350	16	32	700	12	2	0	10	10
Chicken Supreme	250	3	45	500	22	3	8	10	15

Notes:

Calories are the energy value of food. If you eat food with more calories than you use, you will gain weight.

The foods you eat should be low in fat, sodium, and cholesterol.

mg = milligrams
g = grams
% DR = percent of daily amount needed

Name:

Lunchtime 2

Nat wasn't sure which sandwich he should order. The Super Cheeseburger had the most protein, but it also had the most salt and fat. The Fish Sandwich had less fat, but it didn't have as much protein. Nat decided to use a system of points to decide which sandwich was the best one to eat. He added points for cholesterol, calories, salt, and fat. He subtracted points for the nutrients that his body needed. The sandwich with the lowest points was the one he would order.

Nat's Point System

1. Add 5 points for each 50 calories.
2. Add 5 points for each 10 g of fat.
3. Add 5 points for each 10 mg of cholesterol.
4. Add 5 points for each 100 mg of sodium.
5. Subtract 5 points for each 5 g of protein.
6. Subtract the percentage of vitamin A.
7. Subtract the percentage of vitamin C.
8. Subtract 5 points for each 10% of calcium.
9. Subtract 5 points for each 10% of iron.

Nat did not round off the numbers to the nearest 10, 50, or 100. Twenty-four grams of fat, for example, earned 5 points for each 10 grams (2 x 5). The 4 wasn't counted.

1. Predict which sandwich Nat will order. ____________________
2. Tally the score for each sandwich.

   Super Cheeseburger 50 + 10 + 45 + 55 - 25 - 10 - 4 - 5 - 10 = 106

   Deluxe Cheeseburger ____________________

   Fish Sandwich ____________________

   Chicken Supreme ____________________
3. Which sandwich did Nat decide to buy? ____________________

Name:

Aisle Search

Beth's family moved from their apartment to a new house. They needed to build a fence around their yard so they could adopt a dog. While Beth's parents bought the lumber and cement, Beth looked for the other supplies they needed. A sign in the store listed the kinds of merchandise found in each aisle. The aisles were numbered.

Aisle Numbers

Building Tools .... Aisle 6
Lighting .... Aisle 2
Hardware for Gates .... Aisle 3
Paints and Stains .... Aisle 12
Plants .... Aisle 10
Electrical Supplies .... Aisle 15
Nails, Screws, Bolts, Building Hardware .... Aisle 4
Plumbing Supplies .... Aisle 1
Protective Clothing .... Aisle 11
Fireplace Supplies .... Aisle 7
Step Stools and Ladders .... Aisle 5
Garden Supplies .... Aisle 9

Write the aisle number for each item on Beth's list.

two hammers ____________________

drill and drill bits ____________________

ladder ____________________

waterproof stain for the wood ____________________

pliers ____________________

nails, screws, bolts ____________________

a handsaw ____________________

a toolbox ____________________

3 pair of gloves ____________________

hinges and a lock for the gate ____________________

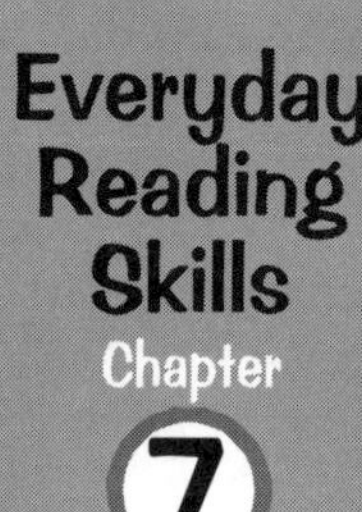

Reading for Details

Reading for details involves pulling out relevant information from the text. This section contains projects that will help students practice this important skill. They will read instructions, plan a garden, and find out the importance of reading when buying a product.

ACTIVITIES

Make a Paper Boat (Pages 53 and 54)
Students read the instructions for making a paper boat and then make a materials and shopping list. This activity is intended to practice reading for details, not as an actual "make-it" project.

Gardening Through the Year (Pages 55–58)
Students use information about specific flowers and vegetables to plan a year-round garden.

Read Carefully! (Pages 59 and 60)
Discover why Samantha should have read more carefully.

Make a Paper Boat

Marta wanted to make a paper boat for a construction contest at school. Before she could build the boat, she had to read the directions to find out what supplies she would need.

Read the directions for Marta's paper boat. List all the needed materials in the space provided on sheet 2. Then follow the remaining directions on sheet 2.

Make a pattern.

1. Cut two rectangles of centimeter graph paper 20 cm long and 8 cm wide for the bottom and top.

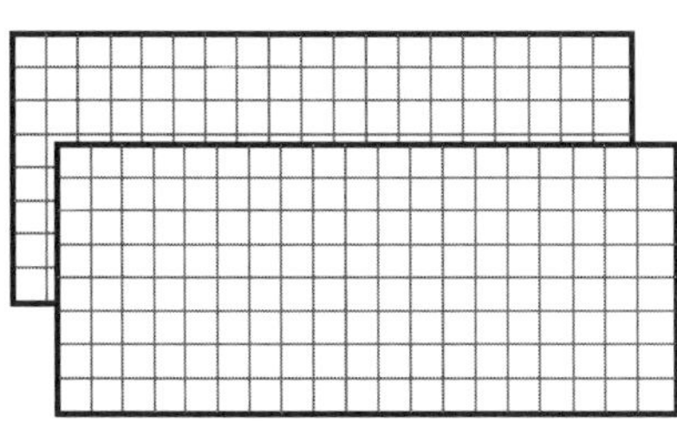

2. Mark the center point on one short side of both bottom and top rectangles.
3. Measure back 6 cm on both long sides. Make marks. Using a ruler and pencil, connect each of these marks.

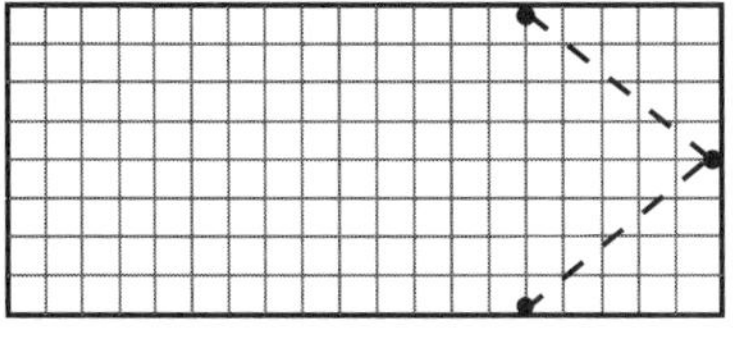

4. The sail is an 8 x 10 cm rectangle cut from corner to corner.
5. For the two sides and the front, cut three pieces that each measure 14 x 5 cm.
6. The back piece is a 8 x 10 cm rectangle.

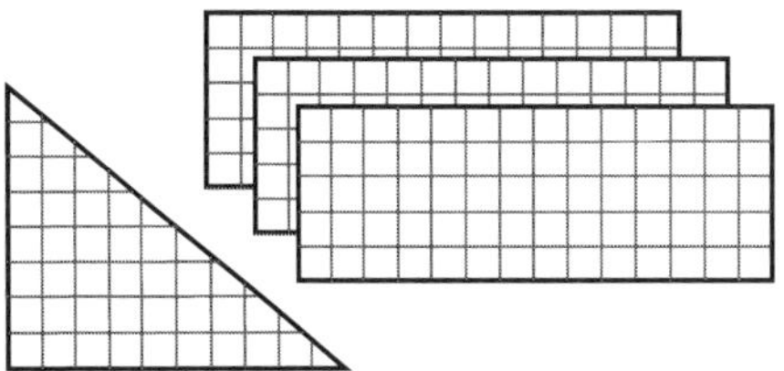

Using the pieces you cut, follow these directions.

1. Cut a 6 cm long, 4 cm wide rectangle from the center of the top deck of the boat.

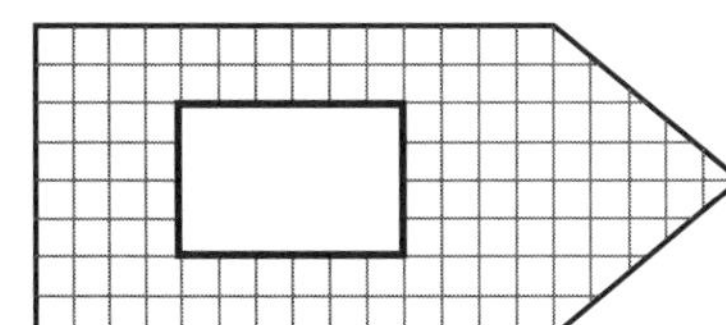

2. Tape all the patterns except the sail to lightweight cardboard or posterboard. Tape the sail pattern to a piece of construction paper. Cut out the pieces.
3. Decorate the pieces using felt pens or crayons. Give your boat a name.
4. Tape all the pieces together. Fold one side piece to fit around the pointed bow.
5. Use the sharp end of a wooden skewer to poke a mast hole into the deck.
6. Glue the sail to the skewer and insert the "mast" through the hole.

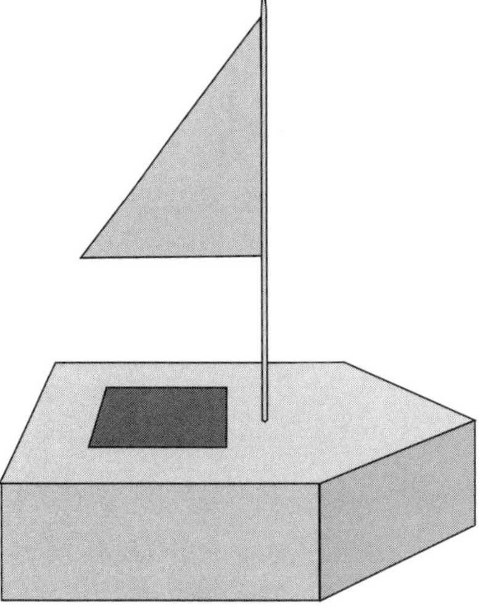

Name:

Make a Paper Boat 2

List all the materials that Marta needs here:

______________________ ______________________

______________________ ______________________

______________________ ______________________

______________________ ______________________

______________________ ______________________

______________________ ______________________

Marta looked in her craft box. This is what she saw.

Help Marta make a shopping list so that she will have all the necessary materials.

Shopping List

____

____

____

____

____

____

____

____

Gardening Through the Year

Arnold lives in a mild California climate area near San Francisco Bay. His parents gave him a sunny area to plant a garden. He can choose what he would like to grow. Arnold wants to have flowers and vegetables growing all the months of the year. He plans to have the tall plants near the fence and the smaller plants in the front so all the plants have sun. He looked up plants in the garden book and made this list of the ones he wants to raise. He wrote down the size of the plants, when he should plant them, and when they would bloom or grow fruits and vegetables.

Flowers

Gladiolus	Blooms from spring to fall. Grows 18–24 inches tall. Plant in October and November.
Daffodil	Plant early to late fall. Many kinds and sizes. Blooms in the spring.
Tulip	Blooms in the spring. Grows 10–12 inches. Plant in the fall.
Snapdragon	Plant in September. Blooms in the winter through spring. Grows 6 inches to 4 feet.
Forget-Me-Not	Blooms in the late spring through fall. Grows 6 to 12 inches. Plant in the spring or fall.
African Daisy	12 to 18 inches tall. Blooms in late fall to early spring.
Wallflower	1 to 2 1/2 feet tall. Blooms from February to May. Plant in the spring.
Chrysanthemum	2 to 3 feet tall. Blooms in June to late summer. Plant in the spring.
Shasta Daisy	Grows 1 to 3 feet. Same bloom cycle as the chrysanthemum.
Common Sneeze-Weed	Blooms in August and September. 6 feet tall.
Perennial Pincushion	Blooms from May through December. Grows to 2 1/2 feet. Plant in the fall.

Gardening Through the Year 2

Larkspur	3 to 4 feet tall. Blooms in the spring. Plant in the fall and winter.
Common Sunflower	7 to 10 feet tall. Plant in the spring. Blooms in the summer and fall.
Zinnia	1/2 to 3 feet tall. Plant when weather is warm. Blooms in the summer and fall.

Fruits and Vegetables

Lettuce	Under one foot. Plant in late summer for winter harvest. Plant in October for spring harvest.
Cabbage	12 to 18 inches tall. Plant in January and February for spring harvest. Plant in July for late fall harvest.
Tomato	2 to 4 feet. Ripens in late summer and fall. Plant in the spring.
Corn	Very tall, 6 to 8 feet. Plant in the spring and harvest in the fall.
Asparagus	Under one foot. Harvest in the spring. New plants every ten years. Plant midwinter.
Broccoli	1 to 2 feet. Cool-weather vegetable.
Pumpkin	1 1/2 to 2 feet. Plant in the spring. Harvest in the fall.
Carrot	Tops grow 9 to 12 inches. Grows during the cool season.
Pea	Plant in the fall or winter. Harvest in the winter or spring. Needs a trellis or 3-foot wire nets to climb.
String bean	Grows during summer months. Plant in the spring. Grows 3 feet tall.

Name:

Gardening Through the Year 3

Use the information on pages 55 and 56 to fill in the chart. List the name of each plant, its size, and when it blooms or produces food.

Arnold's Garden

Name of the Plant	Size	Bloom/Harvest Time

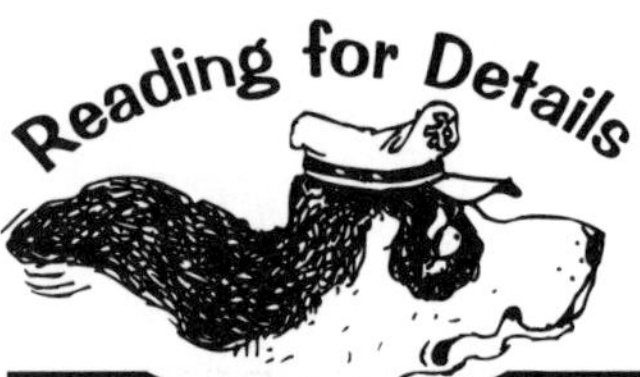

Name:

Gardening Through the Year 4

What will be blooming or producing fruit in Arnold's garden each season? Choose plants from the chart. Remember, the tall plants should be closest to the fence. Write the names of the plants you choose on the garden plans. Include at least five plants for each season.

winter

spring

summer

fall

Read Carefully!

Samantha ordered a new backpack from a catalog. She carried a heavy load of books home from school each day. She needed a large, sturdy backpack. She looked at the pictures in the advertisement and saw one that looked just right. Her choice is circled. After the first week, the straps broke. The company wouldn't refund her money.

A 16

All-purpose.
Blue, red, or green.
Safety pouch inside main compartment.
Weather-resistant nylon.
Holds up to 25 pounds.
Padded shoulder straps.

A 17

School Daze brand. Olive or tan. Large compartment and one outside pouch. Reinforced shoulder straps. Padded for shoulder comfort. Holds up to six pounds.

Aluminum frame overnighter backpack. Side pocket for water bottle. Detachable pouch. Extra-strength straps. Waist belt. Strap for sleeping bag.

A 19

Women's lightweight pack. All-weather coated nylon. Side and back pockets. Large capacity. Padded extra-strength curved shoulder straps. Water bottle strap.

Name:

Read Carefully! 2

Answer the following questions about Samantha's backpack described on page 59.

1. If Samantha had read the description of the backpack carefully, she would not have ordered it. What clues in the advertisement show that it wasn't the right backpack for her?

___

2. Why do you think the company wouldn't refund Samantha's money?

___

3. If Alice wanted to order a backpack for a daytime hiking trip to the state park, which one should she order?

___

Why? ___

4. Omar wanted a backpack for a three-day trip in Yosemite National Park. Which backpack should he order?

___

Why? ___

Now it's your turn. Using your own backpack or a friend's, write an advertisement that a store might use to try to sell it. Be sure to include its brand, what it is made of, and any special features that make it useful. Include an illustration on the back of this page.

___

___

___

___

___

___

___

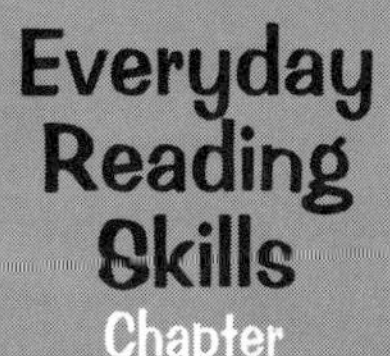

Visualizing What You Read

Visualizing when you read is a very important component of comprehension. The more clearly students "see" what they read, the better able they are to understand. In this section students are asked to turn words into pictures.

ACTIVITIES

Drawing a Map (Page 62)

Students translate directions into a map. You might wish to provide one-inch graph paper if you think students will need to make several attempts.

Picture This (Page 63)

Directions guide students to draw a picture.

Name:

Drawing a Map

Maggie plans to walk to Julia's house Saturday afternoon to work on a science project. On Friday, Julia gave her written directions from the school to her house. Maggie decided to draw a map from the directions. She thought it would be easier to follow the map when she walked to Julia's house.

Read the directions Julia gave to Maggie. Draw a map showing the route from Washington School to Julia's house. Label the streets. Use symbols for the stores, the post office, and the stop sign. You may invent your own symbols. For example, you might write an *S* where the stop sign is or draw a stamped envelope to represent the post office. Draw your symbols on the map legend.

The Directions to Julia's House

- Start at Washington School on the corner of Elm and Walnut.
- Walk three blocks North on Walnut Street.
- Turn to the right on Cedar Street.
- Walk two blocks. You will pass Food Land and the Video Center in the first block. The post office and the park are in the second block.
- Turn right at the stop sign onto Peach Tree Lane.
- Plum Court is in the second block on the right side of the street.
- My house number is 691. It's the second house on the left side of the court.

Legend

Ⓧ Washington School
Food Land
Video Center
Post Office
park
stop sign
Julia's house

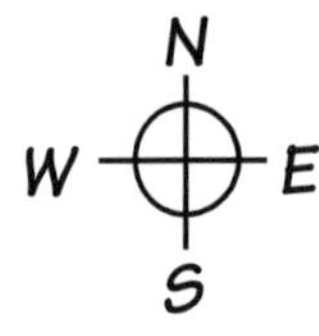

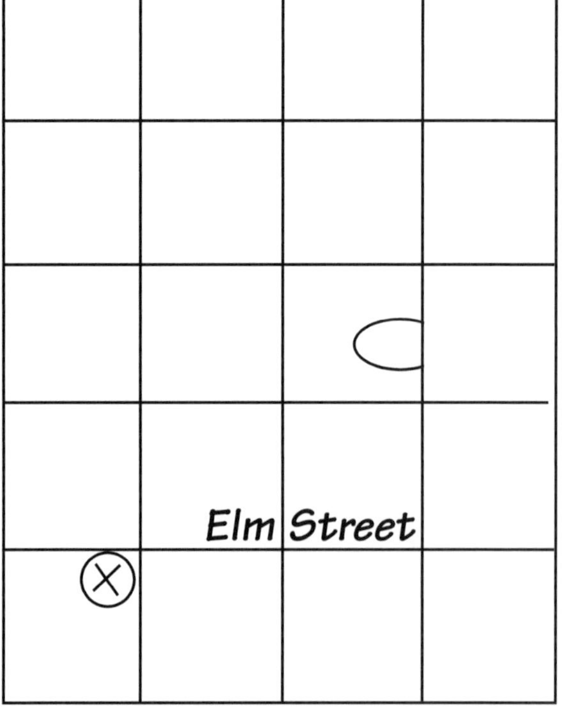

Name:

Picture This

Read the following directions and draw a picture that shows what you read, using very exact measurements. You will need a ruler, pencil, and paper to complete the drawing.

1. Find the middle of Side A. Put a dot there.
2. Extend Side A 1/2" to the left.
3. Using a ruler, connect the end of the 1/2" line to the left end of Side B.
4. Measure up 3" from the dot in the middle of Side A. Make another dot.
5. Connect the two dots with a straight line.
6. Draw a triangle using the line in Step 5 as one side of the triangle and the left side of Side A as the second side. Draw the third side of the triangle connecting the two lines.
7. Form a second triangle. The right side of Side A and the line in Step 5 are two of the sides. Draw the third side to connect the two sides.

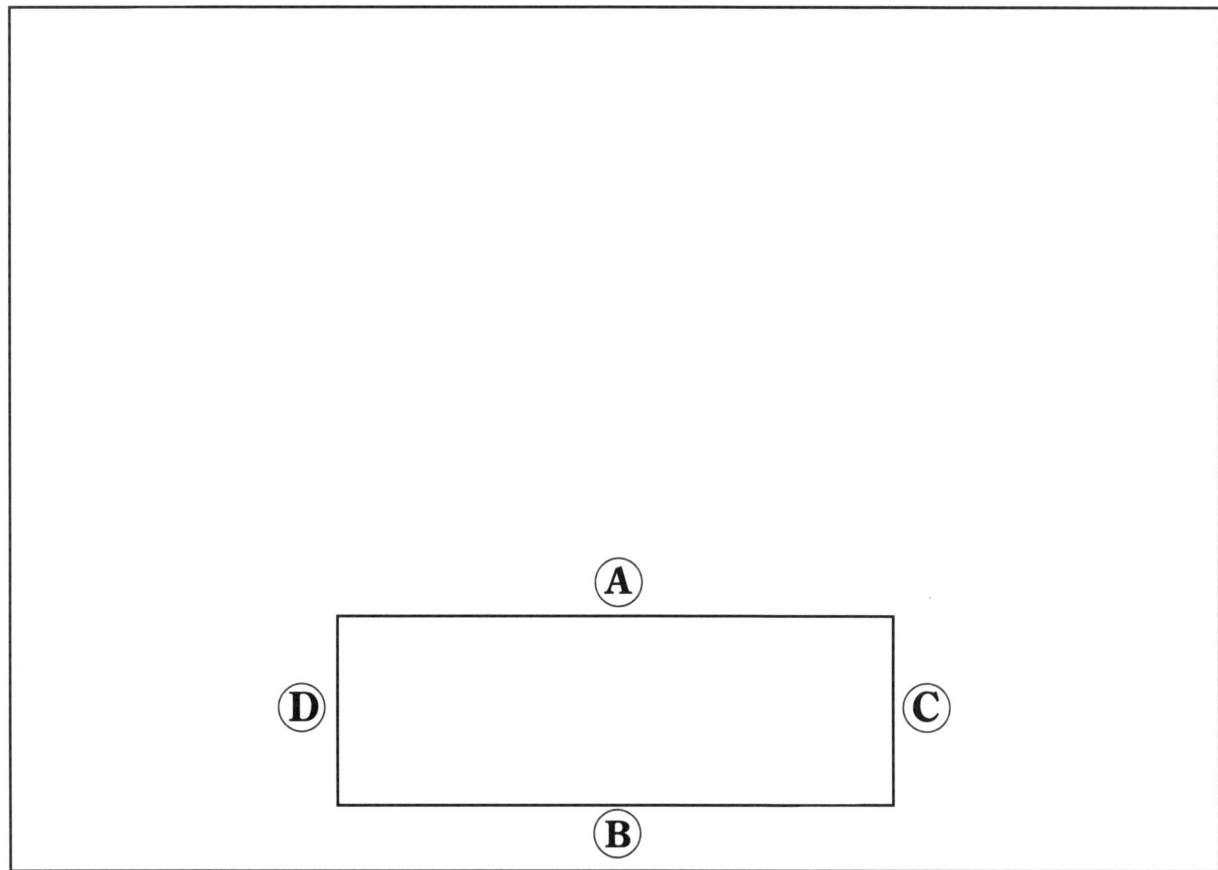

Draw your own picture using a ruler and exact measurements. Write a description and give it to someone. See if the person can duplicate your picture. Good luck!

Schedules

In this section students will do several practice activities that require them to read schedules to find information. Then they will read about a famous American and sequence the important events in his life.

In preparation for reading schedules, collect samples of several types to share with your students. Invite them to bring in schedules they find. You might include:

- a bus schedule
- a television guide
- an advertisement showing the times for movies, concerts, or sporting events
- a pocket calendar with events and appointments marked

While you are working on the activities in this section, make a chart on a large sheet of butcher paper showing your class schedule for the week. Include events occurring daily or weekly and any unusual activities such as field trips, speakers, parties, etc. Post the schedule in class. Go over the schedule at the beginning of each day to review what is going to happen. At the end of the day, read the schedule for the next day as a reminder of what is coming up.

ACTIVITIES

Bay Town Bus Schedule (Page 66)
Use an overhead transparency of the schedule as you ask questions about bus travel. Ask questions about times, which bus to take, costs for one-way and round-trip tickets, arrival and departure times, etc.

Blue Sky Airlines Flight Schedule (Pages 67 and 68)
Use an overhead transparency of the schedule as you ask questions about air travel. Ask questions about arrival and departure times, which flight to take, what gate to go to, etc.

Reproduce the cards on page 68 to use with the airline schedule. Pass out the cards and have students look at the schedule to determine what time they will be "arriving" or "departing."

Television Schedule (Page 69)
Make an overhead transparency to use as you ask questions about television schedules. Ask students to explain what type of information the schedules provide. Provide copies of newspaper television guides or television magazines. Divide the class into groups and have them locate and highlight their favorite programs.

Movie Schedule (Page 70)
Use an overhead transparency and ask students to pretend they are going to the movies. Have them read the movie schedule and explain the kinds of information it provides. Provide newspapers containing a movie guide. Have students work in small groups to determine what is playing at the different theaters and which films they would be allowed to see. Allow time for each group to explain what they find.

My Schedule for This Week (Page 71)
Students use the form to fill in their week's schedule of things to do (dentist appointment, birthday party, Sunday school, soccer practice, scout meeting, school times, etc.).

An Invitation (Pages 72 and 73)
Students read the schedule of events and then answer questions about it.

Bay Town Bus Schedule

Bus Lines

1	Highlands Hospital • Shopping Center Main Street • Park
3	Park West Sundance Lane Discount Shopping
4	Train Connection Airport
14	Bay Town-Oak Hills HWY 99
15	Yosemite Avenue Post Office • Hill School Downtown Bay Town
28	Special Route Aquarium • Wharf

Fares

Cash one-way	$1.00
Day Pass	$4.00
20-Ticket Book	$20.00
Monthly Pass	$30.00

Bus 15 - Yosemite Avenue Stop

Monday through Saturday

5:45 *a.m.*
6:30
7:15
8:00
8:45
9:30
10:15
11:00
11:45

12:15 *p.m.*
1:00
1:45
2:30
3:15
4:00
4:45
5:30
6:15
7:00
7:45
8:30
9:15
10:00
10:45
11:30
12:00 *midnight*

Sundays and Holidays
Every hour
6 *a.m.* - 11 *p.m.*

Blue Sky Airlines Flight Schedule

Arrivals

	Flight	Gate	Time
Boston	127	26	9:05
Carson City	82	16	8:45
Denver	1351	11	9:15
Denver	46	14	10:20
Hawaii	1774	34	9:55
Hollywood	149	29A	10:30
Memphis	198	34	11:50
New York	63	24	8:25
New York	89	27	9:30
Santa Fe	1238	29B	11:00
Seattle	341	20	11:45
Tampa	67	37	9:35
Toronto	85	36	10:40
Wichita	134	28	10:50
Washington, D.C.	57	36	11:40

Departures

	Flight	Gate	Time
Boston	216	36	9:15
Carson City	59	26	9:45
Denver	73	31	8:15
Denver	121	24	10:40
Hawaii	1552	37	9:25
Hollywood	125	28B	10:05
Memphis	152	38	10:35
New York	69	34	11:25
New York	42	31	9:55
Santa Fe	1724	28A	10:20
Seattle	402	29	11:15
Tampa	64	27	9:05
Toronto	29	35	11:20
Wichita	135	28B	11:50
Washington, D.C.	1040	25	11:00

Flight 127 from Boston	Flight 82 from Carson City	Flight 1351 from Denver
Flight 1774 from Hawaii	Flight 89 from New York	Flight 149 from Hollywood
Flight 67 from Tampa	Flight 85 from Toronto	Flight 57 from Washington, D.C.
Flight 216 to Boston	Flight 121 to Denver	Flight 1552 to Hawaii
Flight 42 to New York	Flight 1724 to Santa Fe	Flight 402 to Seattle
Flight 29 to Toronto	Flight 135 to Wichita	Flight 1040 To Washington, D.C.

Television Schedule

T.V. DOG WEEKLY

<table>
<tr><th colspan="8">Tuesday, April 10, 2001</th></tr>
<tr><th>Channel</th><th>3:00</th><th>3:30</th><th>4:00</th><th>4:30</th><th>5:00</th><th>5:30</th><th>6:00</th></tr>
<tr><td>4</td><td colspan="2">Talk About It</td><td colspan="2">Hospital Days</td><td>In the Time of Dinosaurs</td><td>Local News</td><td>News at 6:00</td></tr>
<tr><td>6</td><td colspan="2">Story Time CC</td><td>Puppet Theater CC</td><td>Animals of the Desert</td><td>Freddy & His Friends CC</td><td colspan="2">News Hour CC</td></tr>
<tr><td>11</td><td>Paid Program</td><td colspan="4">Movie: Jungle Adventure (1986)</td><td colspan="2">Beach Buddies</td></tr>
<tr><td>12</td><td>Exercise for Kids</td><td>Around the World</td><td colspan="2">Fairy Tale Films: Ugly Duckling</td><td colspan="2">Today's Sports Review</td><td>News</td></tr>
<tr><td>15</td><td colspan="2">The Cartoon Hour</td><td>Adventures with the Bears</td><td>Cartoon Fun</td><td>Discover Science CC</td><td colspan="2">Kids' Quiz CC</td></tr>
</table>

Movie Schedule

STATE CINEMA CENTER

565 Main Street 374-2581
Bargain Matinees before 5:00 $5.00

Pigs Can Fly (G)

12:45 4:30 7:15 10:00

Wild Horses II (PG-13)

12:30 3:00 6:45 9:30

Sam Smith Jane Jones

Fire Storm (R)

7:00 9:45

Ben Brown Angela Garcia

Dinosaur Park (PG)

4:45 7:00 9:15

Name:

My Schedule for This Week

Fill in this schedule for one week.
Write in the time and activity you need to remember.

Day	Time	Activity
Saturday		
Sunday		
Monday	__:__ to __:__	School
Tuesday	__:__ to __:__	School
Wednesday	__:__ to __:__	School
Thursday	__:__ to __:__	School
Friday	__:__ to __:__	School

An Invitation

May and Joshua received this invitation from their aunt for a weekend at the beach.

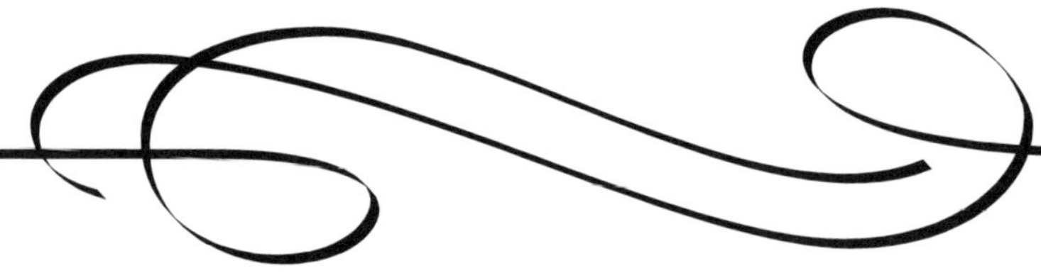

Surf and Sand Weekend

The fun begins at 3:30 on Friday, May 14. Be ready! It's a three-hour drive to Sandy Cove. We'll feast at our favorite fast-food restaurant on the way. After you unpack, it's off to the beach for a marshmallow roast and a look at the stars.

Saturday	7:00 a.m.	Breakfast
	7:45	Head for the beach to see what we can find.
	10:00	Back to the house to check out our treasures.
	11:00	Lunch
	12:00	Downtown to the Ice-Cream Shoppe for dessert and saltwater taffy and then a tour of the souvenir stores.
	1:30	Beach Hike (4 miles round trip). We'll check out the tide pools, see what we can see with the binoculars, and stop at the aquarium for a look at the fish.
	5:00	We're home in time for dinner.
	6:30	We'll walk to the beach and watch the sun sink into the ocean.
	8:00	We'll munch on cookies and play your favorite board games until you fall asleep.

Sunday we'll drive back early in the morning so you can rest up for school.

Love,
Aunt Susan

P.S. I already checked with your mom, and she said you may go.

Schedules

Name:

An Invitation 2

May and Joshua had a fun-filled weekend with Aunt Susan. Answer these questions about their schedule of events.

1. At what time did they arrive in Sandy Cove? ______________________

Was it a.m. or p.m.? ______________________

2. How many hours after breakfast on Saturday did the children and Aunt Susan have lunch?

____

3. How much time was allowed for Saturday's dinner? ______________________

4. At what time do you think Aunt Susan woke the children on Saturday?

____

5. Which activity was allotted the most time? ______________________

How much time was it given? ______________________

6. At what time might Joshua be sipping a chocolate soda? ______________________

7. After such a busy day, at what time do you think May and Joshua fell asleep?

____

8. How much time did Aunt Susan plan for examining things they found at the beach?

____

Everyday Reading Skills Checklist ✓

	Students' Names									
Uses picture content to answer questions										
Observes and evaluates pictures										
Follows picture directions to create an object										
Reads and understands charts										
Follows written directions to: assemble objects										
fill out forms										
learn rules to a game										
Uses alphabetical order to locate information										
Is able to locate information in: the white pages of the telephone book										
the yellow pages of the telephone book										
an address book										
Completes forms and applications accurately and neatly										
Reads with understanding: contest rules										
rebates										
advertisements										
Reads labels and signs with understanding										
Uses label information in a meaningful fashion										
Follows a diagram										
Uses information read to make decisions										
Reads maps with understanding										
Uses schedules to make choices about: transportation										
television										
movies										

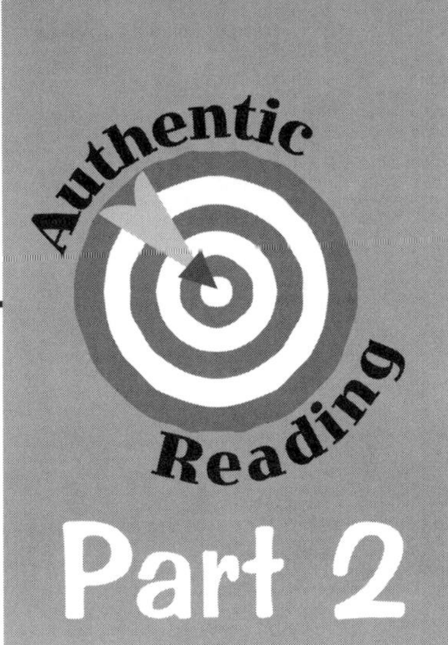

Reading Nonfiction

The activities in this section will help students practice skills such as recognizing main ideas, details, sequencing, drawing conclusions, and summarizing what is read.

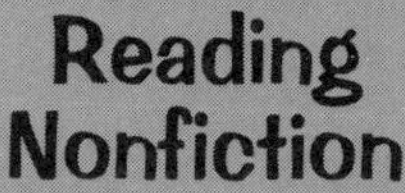

Chapter 1

Asking Questions Before You Read

When students ask questions before they read, it establishes a purpose for reading and helps them locate important information. Thinking about what they want to find out will help them remember details.

The activities in this section suggest questions to ask before reading about events, animals, and people.

ACTIVITIES

Reading About Events (Pages 77–79)
To introduce this activity, reproduce page 77 on an overhead transparency. Pages 78 and 79 present a short article and questions for students to practice finding the answers to who, what, where, when, and why questions.

Reading About Animals (Pages 80 and 81)
To introduce this activity, reproduce page 80 on an overhead transparency. On page 81, students will read an article about the roadrunner to find answers to the chart questions.

Reading Biographies and Autobiographies (Pages 82 and 83)
To introduce this activity, reproduce page 82 on an overhead transparency. Then students read the story about Matthew A. Henson to practice finding the answers to questions about people.

Reading About Events

Asking questions before you read helps you to locate important facts. Different kinds of stories need different types of questions.

You can often use these questions as a guide when you are reading about an event.

Who? (are the people in the story)

What? (happened)

Where? (did it happen)

When? (did it happen)

Why? (did it happen)

Asking Questions Before You Read

Name:

Reading About Events 2

When newspaper reporters write stories, they try to answer these questions:

Who (are the people in the story)
What (happened)
Where (did it happen)
When (did it happen)
and often they add **Why** (did it happen).

You can use these questions as a guide if you are reading about an event. It could be a story about a basketball game, a Fourth of July parade, or something that happened long ago.

The title of the following story is *The White House Burns*. It is written as if it were an article appearing in a newspaper at the time of the event.

Before you read about this event on sheet 3, use the five *who, what, where, when,* and *why* words to write a list of questions about this title. The first two questions have been written for you.

Leave the line under each question blank so you can fill in the answers after you have read the article.

1. Who burned the White House?

   ____

2. What happened when the White House burned?

   ____

3. ______________________________

   ____

4. ______________________________

   ____

5. ______________________________

   ____

Reading About Events 3

The White House Burns

British troops under the command of General Ross and Admiral Cockburn stormed the White House on August 24, 1814. Dolley Madison, the president's wife, fled from Washington City a few hours before the attack. The president was already away.

The British soldiers stuffed souvenirs inside their shirts and uniforms. They piled paintings, draperies, and furnishings in the center of each of the rooms. Even the pianoforte was pushed into the pile.

After the soldiers left the White House, flaming torches, pine poles topped with cotton, were rushed into the president's house. The furniture was set on fire. As the White House went up in flames, the gunpowder stored in the basement exploded. The White House was destroyed along with many other buildings in our nation's capital.

Today, Washington City is a mass of rubble, ashes, and debris. The priceless Congressional Library has been destroyed. Only the U.S. patent office was saved.

Without rereading the story, answer the *who*, *what*, *where*, and *when* questions on page 78 about this news event. Then reread the article to see if your answers match the information in the story.

Challenge

- The article does not tell you **why** the British burned the White House.
- Look for information about the War of 1812 in your library. Find out why the United States and Great Britain were fighting a second war. Write the answer under the **why** question.

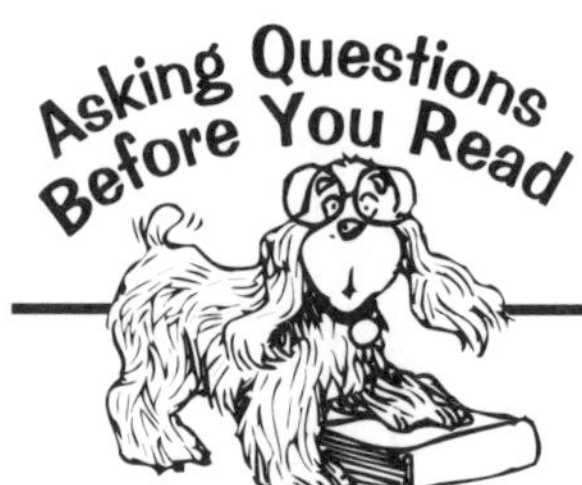

Reading About Animals

Asking questions before you read helps you locate important facts. Different kinds of stories need different types of questions.

You can often use these questions as a guide when you are reading about an animal.

- **To what family does the animal belong?**
- **What does the animal look like?**
- **What does the animal eat?**
- **Where does the animal live? (habitat)**
- **What kind of home does the animal have?**
- **How does the animal raise its young?**
- **What are its enemies and how does it protect itself?**
- **What interesting habits does the animal have?**

Name:

Reading About Animals 2

Study the chart your teacher has provided on *Reading About Animals.* It will help you find information when you read about animals.

Before you read the story about the roadrunner, read the questions that follow the story.

After you have read the story, write the answers to the questions on another piece of paper. If the answer to a question is not in the story, place an X on the line in front of that question.

The Roadrunner

The roadrunner is a bird that doesn't like to fly. It can use its wings in an emergency, but it prefers to walk. This unusual member of the cuckoo family has loose feathers, a strong bill, and a tail that's longer than its body. The first and fourth toes point backward.

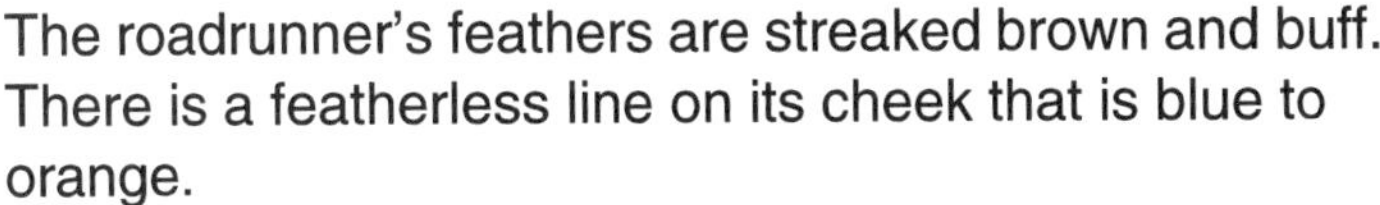

The roadrunner's feathers are streaked brown and buff. There is a featherless line on its cheek that is blue to orange.

The roadrunner hunts rattlesnakes. It stabs the snake with its beak and isn't bothered by the poison. Other popular treats on the roadrunner's menu are grasshoppers, the eggs of other birds, centipedes, scorpions, tarantulas, horned toads, mice, small rats, fruits, seeds, and lizards.

The roadrunner builds a nest in the spring. It chooses a high spot in a cactus or desert bush. The nest is built from snake skins, sticks, roots, leaves, dry manure flakes, and feathers. The female lays three to six white eggs. The male and female birds take turns warming the nest.

______ **1.** The roadrunner is a member of what bird family?

______ **2.** What does the roadrunner look like?

______ **3.** What does the roadrunner eat?

______ **4.** Where does the roadrunner live?

______ **5.** What kind of home or nest does it have?

______ **6.** How does a roadrunner raise its young?

______ **7.** How does a roadrunner protect itself from its enemies?

______ **8.** What interesting habits does the roadrunner have?

Reading Biographies and Autobiographies

Asking questions before you read helps you locate important facts. Different kinds of stories need different types of questions.

You can often use these questions as a guide when you are reading about a person.

Where and when was the person born?

Where and when did the person die?

What were the person's early years like?

What kind of schooling or education did the person have?

What was interesting or important about the person's life?

Name:

Reading Biographies and Autobiographies 2

When you read about a person's life, you are reading a biography (the story of a person's life written by someone else) or an autobiography (the story of a person's life written by that person). Here is a list of biography questions you can use as a guide:

1. Where and when was the person born?
2. Where and when did the person die?
3. What were the person's early years like?
4. What kind of schooling or education did the person have? (Remember that some people had to learn without schools.)
5. What was interesting or important about the person's life?

Read the story about Matthew A. Henson's life. Write the number of the question above the sentence that answers that question. For example, 3 would be written by a fact about Henson's early life. Two of the numbers have been written for you. Numbers may be used more than once. Sentences may have more than one number.

Matthew A. Henson, Explorer

① 

Matthew A. Henson was born in Maryland. His mother died when he was two and his father died six years later. He moved to his uncle's house in Washington, D.C. His uncle cared for him for a few years and also sent him to school.

At thirteen he went to Baltimore and became a ship's cabin boy. The captain of the ship taught him about ships, navigation, geography, and first aid. He traveled all over the world. Wherever he went, he learned about languages and people.

Later, Henson worked on a fishing boat and tried different jobs. Finally, Henson returned to Washington, D.C. He was working as a stock boy in a store when he met Admiral Robert E. Peary. Peary was looking for someone to take part in explorations in the North.

In June 1891, Henson went to Greenland with the admiral. They explored the ice cap. Henson was a valuable member of the expeditions. He worked with Eskimos and also repaired equipment.

Henson was the co-discoverer of the North Pole with Admiral Peary on April 6, 1909.

Finding Information

Students need lots of directed practice before they can use the library confidently and find information in reference materials. This section introduces students to Dewey decimal classification, how to use a table of contents and index, and how to scan for information.

ACTIVITIES

Where Is It in the Library? (Pages 85–87)

Reproduce the Dewey Decimal Classification chart on an overhead transparency. Read it as a class. Ask questions about what topics can be found in various numerical sections. Reproduce pages 86 and 87 for students. They will read about libraries and answer questions about the material read.

The Table of Contents (Page 88)

Discuss the function of a table of contents. Use page 88 to practice using a sample table of contents. Follow up with practice using text or library books.

Using the Index (Page 89)

Answer questions about a sample index. Follow up with practice using text or library books.

Scanning for Information (Pages 90–93)

Students need lots of practice learning to scan for key words when they are looking for specific information. These pages provide practice opportunities to scan both short passages and a longer article. (The story on page 90 will be referred to in the lesson on page 114. You may wish to save the page for use then.)

Dewey Decimal Classification

000–099 GENERAL REFERENCE	Encyclopedias, bibliographies, computer programming
100–199 PHILOSOPHY	Ethics, psychology, philosophy
200–299 RELIGION	Various religions, Bible, myths
300–399 SOCIAL STUDIES	Government, law, fairy tales, folktales
400–499 LANGUAGES	Dictionaries, sign languages, various languages
500–599 SCIENCE	Physics, geology, botany, zoology
600–699 TECHNOLOGY	Inventions, medicine, pets, manufacturing
700–799 ARTS AND RECREATION	Architecture, crafts, sports, music
800–899 LITERATURE	Drama, poetry, humor
900–999 HISTORY	Geography, travel, biography

Name:

Where Is It in the Library?

Read the following paragraphs about libraries. Follow the directions given on sheet 2.

Libraries have number or letter systems to help you find the book you need. The computer listings and library catalogs show a number or letter for each book in the library. To help you find books, the library computers have three alphabetical lists. There is a list with the last names of the authors, another one with book titles, and a list of subjects.

The **Library of Congress** and many colleges and universities use letters for different subjects. The **Dewey decimal system,** which many other libraries use, has a system of numbers. The numbers or letters for a book are found in the library catalogs and computer. The shelves in the libraries are numbered or lettered to help you find the shelf with the book you want. Biographies and autobiographies (books about people) are shelved alphabetically by the person's last name. Books for young people often have a J or a Y in front of the number. Some books are in a special reference section. You can read them in the library, but you can't check them out.

Libraries have magazines, newspapers, videos, tapes, and movies, as well as books. They have microfilm and microfiche machines. Films of books and information can be viewed on these machines. Many libraries have computers that patrons may use to access the Internet.

Name:

Where Is It in the Library? 2

Find It

1. Underline the sentence in the story that tells where you can find the names of books in the library.
2. Circle the way the Library of Congress puts books in order.
3. Draw a box around the way many libraries shelve their books.
4. Draw a triangle in front of the sentence that tells how libraries put biographies in order.

Answer the following questions about libraries.

1. Name the library system that uses numbers.

____

2. Name two kinds of machines that show books and information on film.

____

____

3. List the three ways you can look for books on the library computer.

____

____

____

4. What section of the library has books that can be read in the library, but can't be checked out?

____

Name:

The Table of Contents

In the front of a nonfiction book are the chapters and chapter titles of the book. The following chapters are for a book about the country of Switzerland.

If you want to find out about the Matterhorn, a famous mountain in Switzerland, and there is no index or listing for Matterhorn in the index, you can look through Chapter 1, beginning on page 4, to see if you can spot information on the Matterhorn.

Decide which chapters listed above have information on the following topics. Write the chapter numbers after the topics.

1. Bern, a city in Switzerland ____________________

2. Places tourists could visit ____________________

3. Schools ____________________

4. Food ____________________

5. Mountain lakes ____________________

6. Swiss clocks ____________________

Inside the Chapter

Some chapters have special headings in black print that help you find a section you need. Under the chapter on cities, for example, you would find a section with the heading, *Bern, City of Bears and Flowers.*

The following are headings found in the chapters listed above. List the chapter number for each set of headings.

1. Fruits and Farm Products, Famous Swiss Cheeses Chapter ________

2. Visiting the Lakes, Music Festivals, Historic Buildings Chapter ________

3. Houses, Languages, Work, Entertainment Chapter ________

Name:

Using the Index

Nonfiction books tell true stories. The stories can be about animals, the weather, places, events, history, science, inventions, people, or sports. Nonfiction books are about the world and the universe. They can answer your questions, help with your schoolwork, and show you how to do things.

Sometimes you want to find information for a report or a test at school. There are other times when you might want to read just to find out about a favorite animal or subject. Most nonfiction books have an index in the back of the book. It lists the topics and the important items the author wrote about in the book. The subjects are in alphabetical order.

Here is a sample index from a book entitled *The White House*. On what pages in the book would you find the answers to the following questions? The first question has been answered for you.

1. Where does the president work?

14, 26

2. If you were president, where would you and your family live?

____

3. If the Queen of England were visiting the White House, where would she stay?

____

4. Is green the only color in the Green Room?

____

5. How big is the White House?

____

6. Who designed the White House?

____

The White House

Index

Name:

Scanning for Information

Sometimes there is no table of contents or index. Magazine and newspaper articles are important sources of information without indexes. When you want to find information without these guides, you need to **scan**.

When you scan for information, you don't read every word. Scanning is like looking for a word in a word search puzzle. Here are some steps to follow:

1. Write down or think about **key words** about your subject. For example, if you are trying to find out where an animal lives, you would scan for words like *desert* and *mountains,* or the names of countries and continents.

2. When you see a key word, stop and read the sentence carefully. Does it have the information you need? Sometimes a key word answers another question. When that happens, you need to look further for information.

Scan the following article to find out:

1. **where echidnas live. Circle that sentence.**
2. **what the echidna looks like. Look for color, size, and shape words. Underline these words.**

The Echidna

The echidna is a spiny anteater that lives in Australia. Like all mammals, it is a warm-blooded animal with hair that feeds milk to its young. Because it lays eggs, however, the echidna belongs to a special class of mammals called monotremes.

This unusual animal has a long, thin snout, a small mouth, short legs, and spines that cover its back and sides. The echidna's color is brown. Between its spines it has stiff hairs. The toes on the hind feet have long claws.

The echidna is a nocturnal animal that eats ants and termites. This anteater raids ant nests and termite homes. It digs into the nest, pulls out the insects with its long, sticky tongue, and then crushes them in its mouth. Because the echidna has a small mouth with no teeth, grains of dirt that stick to its tongue help grind up the food.

Name:

More Scanning Practice

Remember, to **scan** for information, you must have **key words** in mind.

Underline key words in the following questions. Number one has been done for you.

To find the answers, scan the sports article that follows the questions. Then write the answers to the questions.

1. Who made the touchdown for Barkley High?

____

2. What was the final score of the game?

____

3. How many touchdowns did Washington score in the last quarter of the game?

____

4. What is the name of the Washington High team?

____

5. Who caught five passes in the game?

____

Washington Upsets Barkley

On Saturday night Washington High trounced football league leader Barkley 41 to 7. Washington scored the first 27 points of the game and added two more touchdowns in the last quarter. The Scorpions' Alan Baker caught five passes and ran 141 yards to keep Washington in the lead. Barkley High, undefeated until they were routed by Washington, scored their only touchdown in the third quarter. Sam Martin ran 23 yards for Barkley's lone TD.

Name:

Scanning a Longer Article

You are going to be scanning a story about Granville T. Woods, a great American inventor, to answer some questions about his life.

- **Read the first question. A key word has been underlined for you.**
- **Scan the article to find the key word. You may need to read the information that comes before and after the key word sentence to find the answer.**
- **Write the answer on the line under the question.**
- **Repeat the process for questions 2 and 3.**

1. At what age did Granville Woods go to work for a <u>blacksmith</u>?

   ____

2. Where did Granville Woods work after he moved to <u>Missouri</u>? (Read the sentence after the key word.)

   ____

3. What did Granville Woods study in night <u>classes</u>?

   ____

- **Now you are on your own. Underline key words in the next three questions and see how quickly you can find the answers. Remember to scan for key words; don't read everything.**

4. What invention did Granville Woods sell to the Bell Telephone Company?

   ____

5. How did Granville Woods improve train safety?

   ____

6. What kind of brakes did Granville Woods invent?

   ____

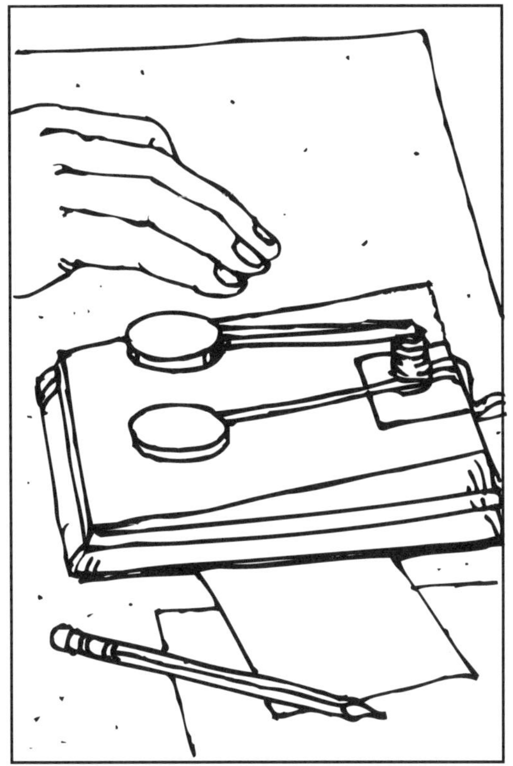

Granville T. Woods

Granville T. Woods was born in 1856 in Columbus, Ohio. He had very little schooling. At age ten he worked as a bellows blower for a blacksmith.

Woods moved with his family to Missouri in 1872. There he worked as a fireman for a railroad. Later he signed on as an engineer on a British steamship.

Woods moved to Cincinnati, Ohio, and opened a machine shop. He manufactured telephone, telegraph, and electrical equipment. He took night classes in mechanical engineering.

In 1884 he improved steam boiler furnaces. He sold his telephone transmitter invention to the Bell Telephone Company of Boston. With the money from the transmitter, he opened the Woods Electric Company.

Many of his inventions improved train safety. He developed a telegraph system that made it possible to send messages between two moving trains. That way, train engineers would know when another train was on the same track. His invention prevented many train accidents.

In 1890 he moved to New York City and spent a lot of his time working on his inventions. He developed an electric third rail for streetcars. It reduced friction and made electric rail travel safer. He produced 14 more inventions for electric railways. The automatic air brake system he invented was sold to the Westinghouse Air Brake Company. Another important Woods invention was a safety cutoff device for electrical circuits.

Granville T. Woods' inventions made our lives safer and improved communication systems. He applied for and received more than 50 patents for his inventions.

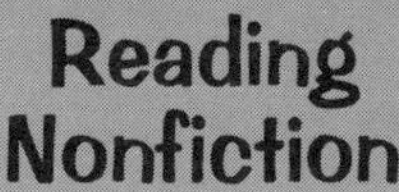

Chapter 3

Recording and Organizing Information

This section shows students how to record and organize the information they find. Activity pages demonstrate mapping information to include main ideas and details.

ACTIVITIES

Mapping the Main Idea (Pages 95 and 96)
Practice finding the main idea of each paragraph in a selection. Page 96 suggests how students can use the questions they formulated before reading (pages 76–83) to help locate main ideas.

Adding Details to an Information Map (Page 97)
Students read a list of details and decide under which main idea each should be written.

Mapping the Main Ideas and Details (Pages 98 and 99)
Students read a story about the eruption of Mount St. Helens. They then fill in an information map with the main idea and details given in each paragraph.

Mapping Information Form (Page 100)
Use this blank mapping form to practice making information maps using other sources. To help students separate the main ideas and details, the main ideas are enclosed in boxes and the details placed in circles.

Recording & Organizing Information

Name:

Mapping the Main Idea

An information map is a great way to remember what you read. An information map looks like this:

Topic or Subject
The Amazon River

The **topic** or subject is what you are reading about. For example, the subject for the next story is the Amazon River.

The **main idea** tells what the paragraph is all about. Everything in the paragraph should be about that idea. Usually the main idea will be in the first or last sentence in the paragraph, but it can be in the middle of the paragraph.

Read the three paragraphs about the Amazon River. Decide which sentence in each paragraph is the main idea. Underline the main idea sentence. The first one has been underlined for you.

The Amazon River

The Amazon River in South America is one of the world's great rivers. It meanders through the tropical rainforest for 4,195 miles. At times, this slow-moving waterway looks more like a lake than a river. When the water level is low, it averages one to seven miles in width. During floods its width can measure 30 miles from one side to the other. The depth of the river ranges from 200 feet to a few inches where sandbars have been formed from sediment in the water. When the water level is high, the Amazon can rise 50 feet above its normal level.

The Amazon has more tributaries than any other river in the world. Rivers from the high Andes Mountains and the highlands to the north flow into the Amazon. Approximately 1,100 tributaries join the great river. Together, they pour an average of six million cubic feet of water into the Atlantic Ocean every second.

Each day, the Amazon deposits tons of food-laden silt in the ocean. The rotted vegetation in the silt is swept out to sea. It provides food for the fish and plankton in the Atlantic Ocean and the Caribbean Sea. People who live over a thousand miles away eat fish nourished by the Amazon River.

Write the main idea from each paragraph in the following information map boxes.

Paragraph 1 Main Idea	Paragraph 2 Main Idea	Paragraph 3 Main Idea

Name:

Mapping The Main Idea 2

Using Your Questions

If you have written out questions you want to answer when you read, you can use the answers you find for the main ideas in your map. The following are examples from information about the echidna.

- **To what family does the echidna belong?**
- **What food does the echidna eat?**

topic or subject:

The Echidna

main idea:

The echidna belongs to the family of animals called monotremes.

main idea:

The echidna eats ants and termites.

Now You Try It

Here are two questions a student might have asked about black bears. Use the answers to begin an information map. Remember to write the topic, **Black Bears**, in the top rectangle.

- **What do black bears look like?**
  Black bears are the smallest bears in North America.
- **What do black bears eat?**
  Black bears are omnivores.

topic or subject:

main idea:

main idea:

Recording & Organizing Information

Name:

Adding Details to an Information Map

When you read about people, animals, places, events, and objects, you will find many facts about the main ideas. These pieces of information are called **details**. When you want to remember the details, add the information to the main ideas on the map.

Here is the information map you have created on the topic Black Bears. Read the details at the bottom of the page. Write each detail in a circle under the correct main idea.

Black Bears

Black bears are the smallest bears in North America.

Black bears are omnivores.

Details

- Black bears eat grasses, herbs, and skunk cabbage.
- Black bears eat animals that die during the winter.
- Females weigh from 120 to 180 pounds.
- Black bears eat nuts and berries.
- Males weigh from 250 to 350 pounds.

Mapping the Main Ideas and Details

Here is a story about Mount St. Helens, an active volcano in the state of Washington, U.S.A. In both paragraphs the first sentence gives the main idea of that paragraph.

Read the story. Then follow the directions on page 99 to organize the details under the correct main idea.

Mount St. Helens Explodes

The eruption of Mount St. Helens on May 18, 1980, caused widespread destruction. Tons of ash, ice, and rock shot out of the volcano. Steam and rock roared 60,000 feet into the air. Lightning bolts and flaming cinders set off forest fires. Nearby Spirit Lake became a boiling mass of mud and debris. Melting snow and ice flowed down the volcano's slopes. Mud slides blocked the rivers and caused floods. Mudflows carried away logs and houses. The mud and debris covered roads, bridges, and buildings.

Signs of the explosion traveled long distances. The eruption blocked out the light of the sun in Spokane, Washington, miles away. Neighboring states were blanketed by falling ash. A light volcanic dust drifted as far away as northern Virginia, settling on cars and houses.

Name:

Mapping the Main Ideas and Details 2

You have read a story about the eruption of Mount St. Helens. Fill in the main idea of each paragraph and then write each detail from the box below under the correct main idea. (Remember that in this story the first sentence of each paragraph gives the main idea of the paragraph.)

Paragraph 1

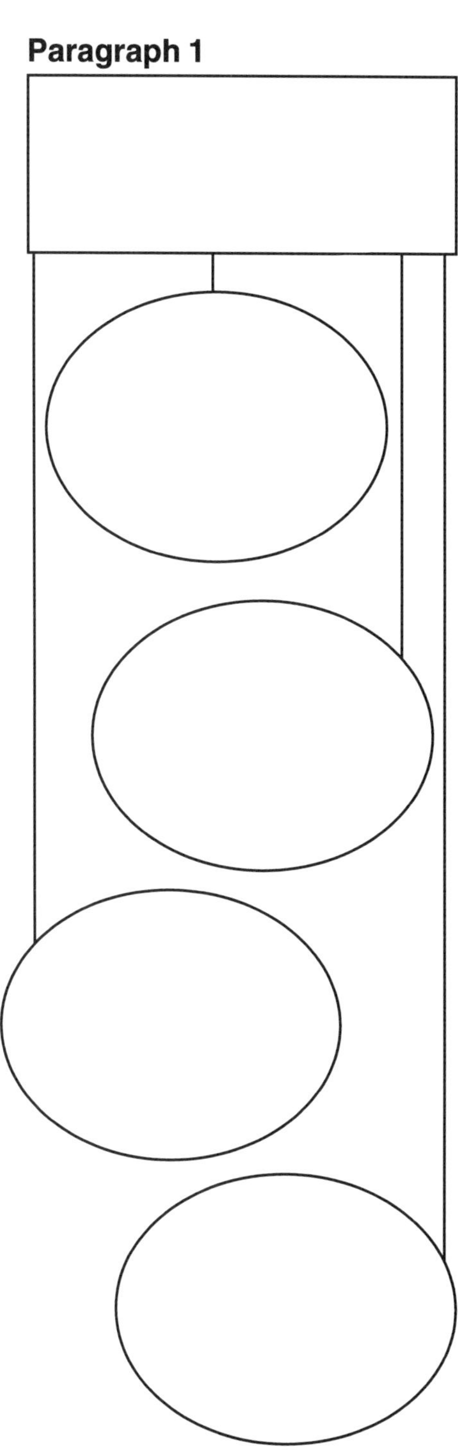

Paragraph 2

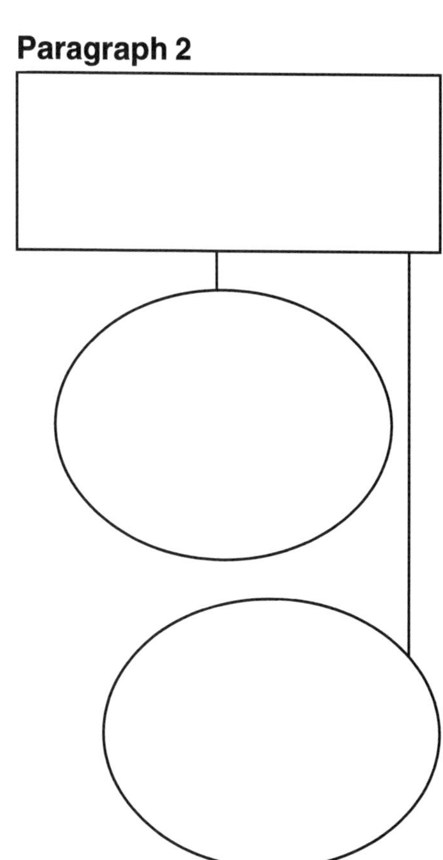

Details
- blocked out sunlight in Spokane, Washington
- steam, rock 60,000 feet up
- volcanic dust as far as Virginia
- mud, debris covered roads, bridges, buildings
- lightning, flaming cinders caused forest fires
- Spirit Lake a mass of mud, debris

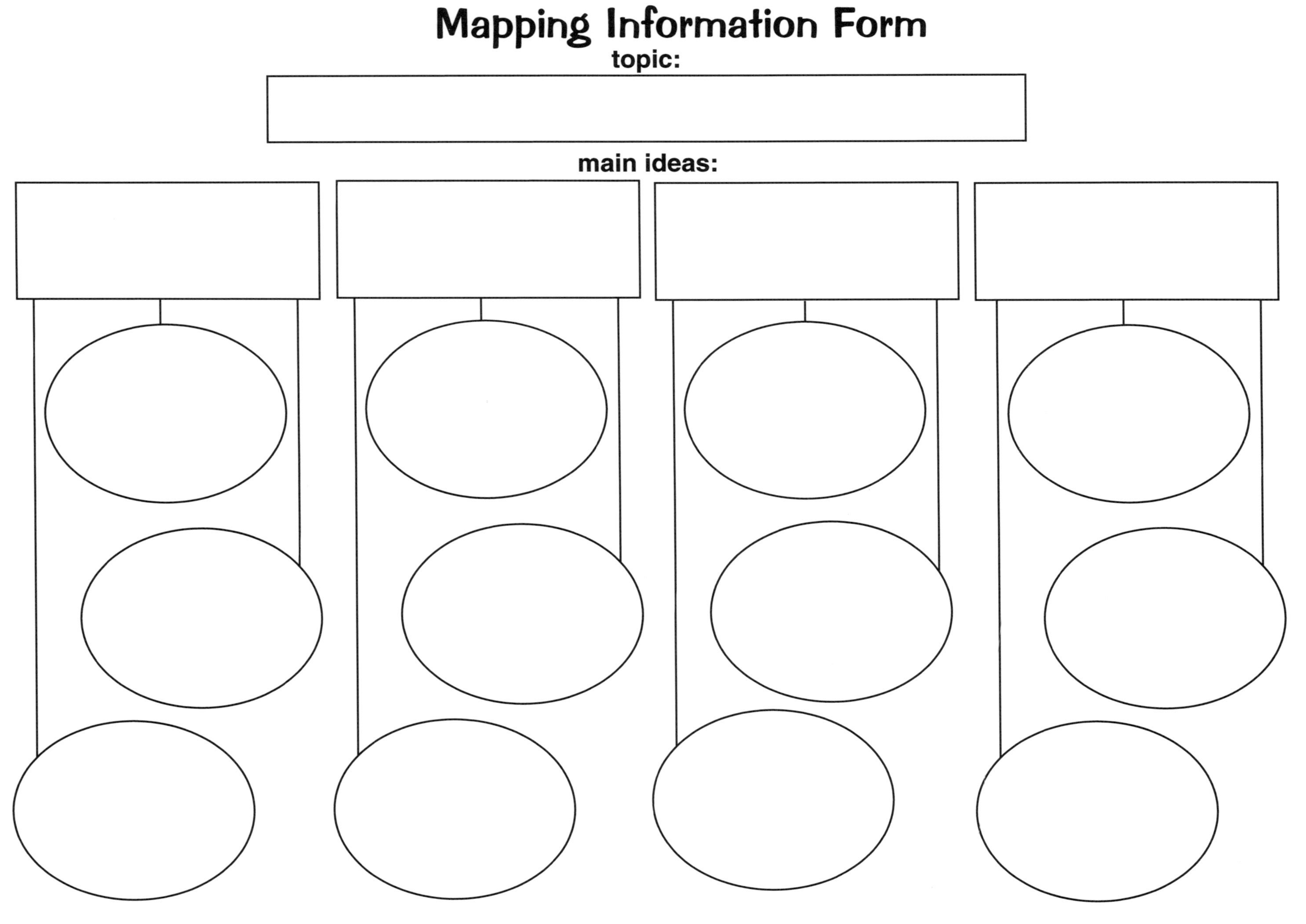
Mapping Information Form
topic:
main ideas:

Sequencing Information

Stories that students will read are often not written in chronological order. Being able to sequence that information is a necessary skill that requires practice.

ACTIVITIES

Sequencing Practice (Pages 102 and 103)

These exercises provide practice sequencing stories in chronological order.

Benjamin Franklin (Pages 104–106)

Students read the biographical information and take notes on dates and events mentioned. These notes are transferred to the boxes on page 106 and then pasted to a time line. Adding machine tape is a good choice for the time line. Students mark one year every two inches (five centimeters). The time line boxes may be glued directly on the tape. In this way, the time relationship of events is easily seen.

Name:

Sequencing Practice

The events in stories are not always written in chronological (by time—first, second, third, etc.) order. You must read carefully to decide the order of events in a story.

The following sentences are from a biography about George Catlin, who painted pictures of Native Americans during the late 1800s.

Number the sentences chronologically from 1 to 8. Some of the details have been numbered for you.

George Catlin

1 George Catlin was born in 1796.

8 He died in 1872.

_____ He did not like being a lawyer so he began painting pictures of people.

_____ When he was a young man, he became an apprentice to a lawyer to learn about laws.

_____ Today, his paintings and journals are important records that show how Native Americans lived in the 1800s.

3 He opened his own law practice in Pennsylvania.

5 He decided to travel with his brushes and paints to American Indian settlements in the west.

_____ He spent the rest of his life painting and writing about North and South American Indians.

Name:

Sequencing Practice 2

After an entire school year of fund-raising, Steve Student's class is finally ready for the big field trip. Steve decided to write about the experience. Unfortunately, all of his note cards got mixed up. Help Steve put his notes in order so that he can write his report.

Number the following events chronologically.

Fill in the words in the last sentence to tell where the class is going. It should be the best field trip you can imagine.

____ I stuffed everything I needed into my backpack, including my lunch, a day's supply of peanut clusters, and a bottle of water.

____ Sammy was my seat partner on the train.

____ The two sixth-grade classes had a whole coach all to themselves.

____ I walked to the train depot where I met the other students in the class.

____ The sixth-grade classes had been raising money for the big June field trip all year.

____ The conductor helped us onto the train.

____ Sammy sold the most holiday candles and I sold the most peanut clusters.

____ The teacher checked off our names and handed us our tickets.

____ It was a two-hour ride to ______________________________ .

Challenge

Write a paragraph with at least three sentences about the rest of the field trip. Write the sentences in chronological order.

____

____

____

____

____

____

____

Benjamin Franklin

When you read an interesting story, the writer doesn't always begin with the event that happened first. For example, John visited the Grand Canyon in August. When he told his class about his trip, he described what he saw at the Grand Canyon first. Then he talked about traveling on the train to Arizona and getting ready for the trip.

Read this biography about a famous American. The events in the story are not necessarily in chronological order. You will then follow instructions on sheets 2 and 3 to complete a time line of Franklin's life.

Benjamin Franklin

Benjamin Franklin was a great inventor. When he was 77, he invented bifocal glasses so he could read books and see objects that were far away without changing glasses. When he was 35, he invented the Franklin Stove so people could have heat from a wood-burning stove in the center of the room. His famous kite experiment in 1752 proved that lightning is electricity.

Franklin enjoyed writing. He published his own newspaper, *The Pennsylvania Gazette,* when he was 23. He started the first public library in the American colonies and published *Poor Richard's Almanack* when he was 25. Franklin became interested in newspapers when he was 12. He was sent to live with his older brother, James, to learn about printing newspapers. When he was 16, he secretly wrote humorous stories for his brother's newspaper.

Franklin worked to improve the lives of people who lived in the colonies. When he was 47, he organized a better mail-delivery system. He petitioned Congress to end slavery in 1789.

Franklin was well known in England and France. In 1757 he went to England to gain more freedom for the people living in America. When he was 60, he convinced the British Parliament to end the Stamp Act, which added taxes to printed documents and materials bought by the colonists.

During the American Revolutionary War, when Franklin was 70 years old, he became minister to France. The French helped the colonists win their freedom from England. Six years later, at the end of the war with England, Franklin helped write the peace treaty. He had also been one of the signers of the Declaration of Independence in 1776. He was an important member of the Constitutional Convention in Philadelphia when he was 81 years old.

Benjamin Franklin died in Philadelphia in 1790 when he was 84 years old.

Sequencing Information

Name:

Benjamin Franklin 2

On each of the lines below, write a few words about something Benjamin Franklin did, or list an event in his life. Three entries have been made for you. The entries do **not** need to be in chronological order. Write a date in each of the boxes. The date of his birth has been given in the first box. To arrive at this date, Franklin's age (84) was subtracted from the year he died (1790). If Franklin's age is given instead of the year of the event, add his age at that time to 1706, his birth date.

Example: He was 70 years old when he became minister to France.
Add 70 to 1706. He became minister to France in 1776.

Event	Date
Benjamin Franklin was born.	1706
Started first public library. Published Poor Richard's Almanack.	1731
Petitioned Congress to end slavery.	1789

Now transfer the information to the boxes on sheet 3. Cut out the boxes. Arrange them in chronological order on a large piece of paper or strip of adding machine tape. Glue them in place. Add a title and illustrations.

Benjamin Franklin 3

1706 Benjamin Franklin was born.	**1731** Started first public library. Published *Poor Richard's Almanack*.	**1789** Petitioned Congress to end slavery.

Notes and Outlines

Note-taking and outlining are difficult skills for students to acquire. The step-by-step lessons in this section will help clarify the whys and hows of these important skills.

ACTIVITIES

What Is Note-Taking? (Page 108)
Create an overhead transparency to read with the class and discuss what it means to take notes.

Learning to Take Notes (Pages 109 and 110)
More Note-Taking Practice (Pages 111 and 112)
Students read a story, evaluate the completeness of notes taken on the story, and add notes of their own.

Completing an Outline (Pages 113 and 114)
Make an overhead transparency of page 113 to introduce what an outline is. Page 114 presents an outline of the story of the echidna from page 90. Refer to the story as you discuss parts I and II of the outline. Complete part III using information contained in paragraph 3 of the story. This paragraph is also presented at the bottom of page 114.

Putting It All Together—Notes, Maps, and Outlines (Pages 115–117)
Students use a set of notes to construct an information map and an outline.

Using Several References (Pages 118–120)
Students use information presented from three sources to complete a set of notes and an outline.

Your Review Guide (Page 121)
Give students a copy of this page to keep in their writing folders. They may refer to it as they do other projects on nonfiction reading.

Outline Form (Page 122)
This blank outline form may be used for additional outlining practice.

What Is Note-Taking?

When you are finding information so that you can write a report, it's necessary to record some of the information in order to remember it. But you don't want to write complete sentences—that takes too much time. Besides, it is not proper to use someone else's exact words. So you must learn to take notes.

Notes are short statements of important ideas (key words). Notes are not complete sentences. You may leave out any words that do not change the meaning.

This is **not** a note:

> The roadrunner builds a nest in the spring. It chooses a high spot in a cactus or bush.

This **is** a note:

> nest in spring, high in cactus or bush

Here are two examples of how to take notes on information that answers questions you have asked about a topic.

Sally Student wants to report on spiders. One of the questions she wants to answer is "How do spiders care for their young?" She wrote the question on a piece of paper and recorded the information she found. Notice that she did not write complete sentences.

How do spiders care for their young?

1. many wrap eggs in silk egg sacs called cocoons - protects eggs
2. some stay until babies hatch, not eating
3. some female spiders leave after eggs are in cocoons
4. wolf spider carries cocoon until babies hatch - then they ride on her back

Sammy Student is going to report on black bears. One of his questions is "What does the black bear look like?" Here is a paragraph that he read and the notes that he took.

The front claws of the black bear are shorter and more curved than the claws on its back feet. Unlike those of a cat, the claws are not retractable. The front feet are shaped like a human hand, and the back feet are like a human foot.

Notes:

1. front claws shorter, more curved
2. claws not retractable
3. front feet like human hand
4. back feet like human foot

Learning to Take Notes

When you need to remember a lot of information for a report, you can take shortcuts. Instead of writing complete sentences, just write enough so you will remember the main ideas and the details. Leave out the unimportant words.

To begin learning about taking notes, read the following story about the reporter Nellie Bly.

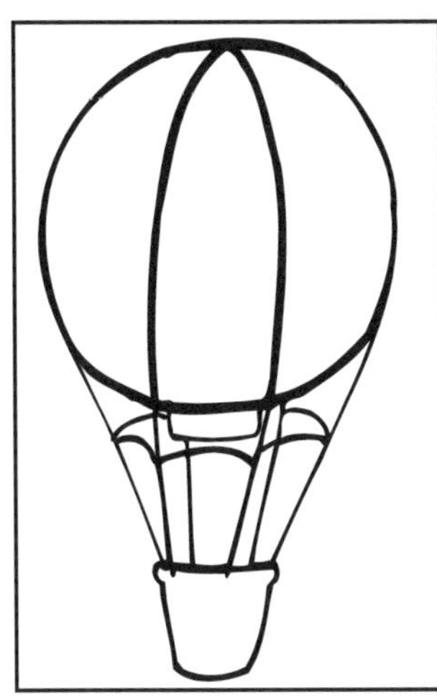

Nellie Bly

Elizabeth Cochrane was born in 1867. She was 18 years old when she went to work as a writer for the *Pittsburgh Dispatch,* a newspaper in Pittsburgh, Pennsylvania. She used the pen name Nellie Bly. (Sometimes authors use pen names instead of their own names.) She wrote about social problems in the city. People read her articles about conditions in the factories and housing for the poor. Her readers helped make changes that improved the lives of many people.

She went to work for the *New York World* newspaper in 1887. She pretended to be mentally ill and was sent to Blackwell's Island asylum as a patient. She found that the patients were mistreated and many people did not belong there. She wrote about her experiences. People were shocked when they learned about the conditions there. Her article brought many needed changes.

On November 14, 1889, Nellie Bly sailed out of New York harbor. She set out to see if she could beat the 80 day around-the-world record of Phileas Fogg. Fogg was a fictional character in Jules Verne's book *Around the World in Eighty Days.* She traveled by ship, train, sampan, horse, burro, stagecoach, and jinricksha. She made the trip in 72 days, 6 hours, 11 minutes, and 14 seconds. In 1890 she wrote the book *Around the World in 72 Days.*

She married a millionaire, Robert Seaman, in 1895. When he died, she ran his manufacturing plant. The business failed in 1913.

In 1914 Nellie went to Europe. Because of World War I, she was interned there and had to stay until the end of the war.

She went to work for the *New York Journal* after the war. Nellie Bly died on January 27, 1922.

Name:

Learning to Take Notes 2

Here are some notes taken from the story about Nellie Bly. Some of the notes do not give enough information. Make an X in front of these notes and then rewrite them on the lines below. Add details so the facts are complete.

_____ **1.** Born

_____ **2.** newspaper writer

_____ **3.** Elizabeth Cochrane real name — Nellie Bly pen name

_____ **4.** wrote about social problems

_____ **5.** her stories caused people to change the way things were done

_____ **6.** worked for *New York World* newspaper in 1887

_____ **7.** went to Blackwell's Island, an asylum for the mentally ill, as a patient

_____ **8.** mistreated

_____ **9.** her article helped bring about better conditions

_____ **10.** set out Nov. 14, 1889, to beat 80 days around world record of Phileas Fogg, character in Jules Verne novel, *Around the World in Eighty Days*

_____ **11.** traveled

_____ **12.** returned

_____ **13.** married

On the lines below, rewrite the notes that do not give enough information.

____

____

____

____

____

____

Add three notes of your own about Nellie Bly. Make sure you do not repeat any of the details given in notes 1–13. Remember, use only the words that are needed.

14. ______________________________

15. ______________________________

16. ______________________________

Name:

More Note-Taking Practice

When you take notes, you will often be writing on small cards or in narrow rows on charts where there isn't much room. You need to write only the most important words. Any word that is not necessary for the meaning should be left out. You can use commas and dashes to separate parts of the note.

Rewrite each complete sentence below as it might appear on a note-taking card. The number in parentheses gives the number of words to try for. Number one has been done for you.

1. The jaguar, a member of the cat family, has a brownish-yellow coat marked with many dark spots. (7)

   jaguar - cat family - brownish-yellow, dark spots

2. Sojourner Truth traveled far and wide speaking against slavery, even visiting President Abraham Lincoln at the White House. (8)

   ____

3. The moon is smaller in size than the earth and covered with grayish rocks and fine dust. (7)

   ____

4. Koalas, whose name means "no drink" in Aboriginal language, are found in eucalyptus forests of the coastal areas of northeastern and southeastern Australia. (11)

   ____

5. Besides being a tasty and healthful food, peanuts can be used to make soap, face powder, shaving cream, shampoo, and paint. (12)

   ____

6. Christopher Columbus was convinced that if he could sail around the globe, he would prove that the earth was a sphere, not flat as many believed. (10)

   ____

7. A rhinoceros rests most of the day and is active at night, when it eats grass, leafy twigs, and shrubs. (11)

   ____

Name:

More Note-Taking Practice 2

Sally Student's friend Sarah read a short article about comets. Then she took notes on the article. Sarah didn't know that when you take notes you should write only the most important words, so her notes are in complete sentences.

Rewrite Sarah's notes using only the necessary words. The first one has been done for you.

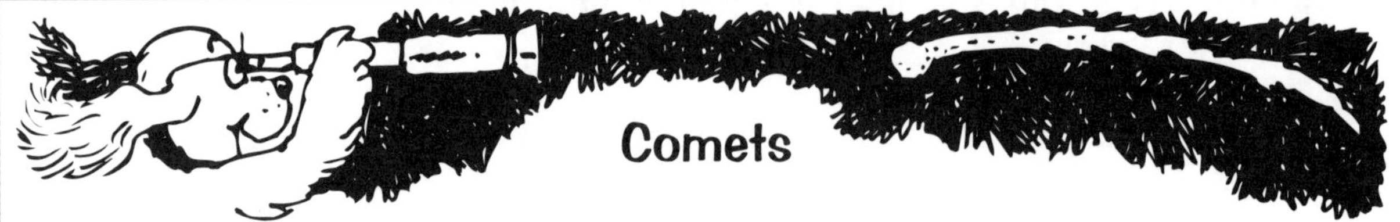

Comets

A comet is a chunk of ice, dirt, and rock. As a comet nears the sun, the ice is melted and then evaporates to form a gas. The gas, dust, and debris jets out away from the comet. It forms a gas cloud called a coma. This coma or tail can stretch out for a million miles. We see the coma when the comet nears the sun.

Comets become millions of tons lighter after a trip around the sun. The dust and gas they lose can be pulled to other planets or drift in space.

Some comets visit the sun once, then shoot out into space. Others, like Halley's comet, make return visits. Halley's comet will be closest to the sun again on July 28, 2061. It takes 76 years for Halley's comet to complete its orbit.

1. Comets are chunks of ice, dirt, and rock. made of ice, dirt, rock

2. The coma or tail is made up of gas. ____________________

3. A coma can be a million miles long. ____________________

4. A comet is smaller after traveling around the sun because it loses tons of dust and gas.

____

5. Some comets visit the sun once, but others return. ____________________

6. Halley's comet returns to the sun every 76 years. ____________________

7. Halley's comet makes its next return trip around the sun in 2061. ____________________

____

Completing an Outline

An **outline** is a way of organizing information that can help you write a report or story. In a way it's like a skeleton—it holds a body of information together and keeps it in order.

- At the top of an outline is the title. That's the **heading**.
- Next come the questions or **main ideas,** which are written after **Roman numerals**.
- Indented **capital letters** written under the main ideas keep the **details** in order.
- Sometimes there is special information about the details. These facts are numbered.

Here is a "bare bones" outline.

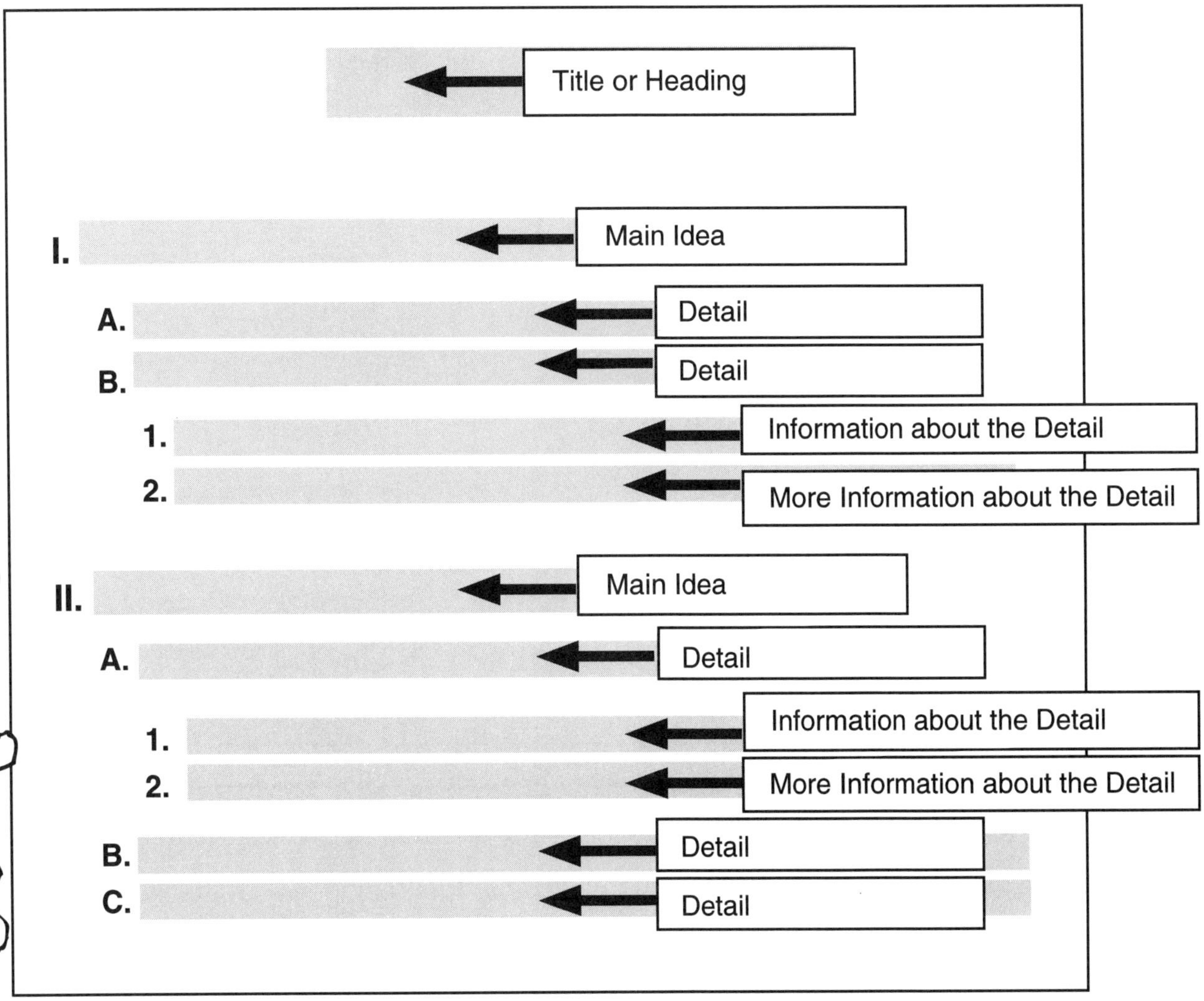

← Title or Heading

I. ← Main Idea
- A. ← Detail
- B. ← Detail
  1. ← Information about the Detail
  2. ← More Information about the Detail

II. ← Main Idea
- A. ← Detail
  1. ← Information about the Detail
  2. ← More Information about the Detail
- B. ← Detail
- C. ← Detail

Name:

Completing an Outline 2

Here is the beginning of a sample outline for a report on the echidna, an Australian animal. Use the paragraph following the outline to complete part III of the outline.

- **Notice that each line begins with a capital letter.**
- **Write in note form—use necessary words only.**

The Echidna

I. Is a monotreme

A. Warm-blooded
B. Feeds its young milk
C. Lays eggs

II. Unusual animal

A. Long, thin snout
B. Small mouth
C. Short legs
D. Spines cover back and sides
E. Stiff hairs between spines
F. Hind feet toes have long claws
G. Is brown

III. Eats ants and termites

A. ______________________________
B. ______________________________
C. ______________________________
D. ______________________________

The echidna is a nocturnal animal that eats ants and termites. This anteater raids ant nests and termite homes. It digs into the nest, pulls out the insects with its long, sticky tongue, and then crushes them in its mouth. Because the echidna has a small mouth with no teeth, grains of dirt that stick to its tongue help grind up the food.

Putting It All Together
Notes, Maps, and Outlines

Sally, Sammy, and Sarah's classmate Stanley Student decided to do a report on Phillis Wheatley, the first African-American woman poet to be published.

Stanley read a book and took notes about Phillis Wheatley's life. However, he doesn't think he will get his report done on time without some help on the information map and the outline. This is where you come in:

 **Read Stanley's notes.**

 **Complete his information map on sheet 2.**

 **Use the information map to complete his outline on sheet 3.**

Notes on Phillis Wheatley

Early Life

Born in Africa
Captured, brought to America as slave when 8 or 9
Bought by John Wheatley in Boston

Her Poetry

First poem age 13
Wrote poem for Mary's wedding
Boston people wanted poems written for them
Traveled to England - poems published in 1773

Life as a Slave

Companion for the Wheatley twins, Mary and Nathaniel
Helped Mrs. Wheatley, an invalid
Taught to read and write
Given freedom in 1772 when about 20

Her Later Life

Married John Peters
Had three children, two died
Husband taken to debtors' prison
She and her baby died, December 1784

Name:

Putting It All Together 2

Stanley was planning to make an information map before he wrote an outline. The map would organize the details under the main ideas.

Lend Stanley a hand and make an information map from the notes about Phillis Wheatley.

Phillis Wheatley

Early Life	Life as a Slave	Her Poetry	Her Later Life

Name:

Putting It All Together 3

Use your completed information map to write an outline about Phillis Wheatley.

I. ____________________
  A. ____________________
  B. ____________________
  C. ____________________
II. ____________________
  A. ____________________
  B. ____________________
  C. ____________________
  D. ____________________
III. ____________________
  A. ____________________
  B. ____________________
  C. ____________________
  D. ____________________
IV. ____________________
  A. ____________________
  B. ____________________
  C. ____________________
  D. ____________________

Challenge

- Using your outline about Phillis Wheatley as a guide, tell a group of students in another class about her life.
- Use the outline about the echidna to write a short report.

Using Several References

Sometimes the book or story you are reading does not answer all your questions. Then you need to read more than one book or story to find the answers.

Salvatore Student is going to the Hawaiian Islands for a vacation. He will spend time on the island of Hawaii. The only thing he knows about the island is that it is called "The Big Island." His friend Serena thinks there may be volcanoes there. Salvatore thinks he will enjoy his trip more if he learns more about the island before the trip. Here are the questions he wants to answer:

- Why is Hawaii called "The Big Island"?
- Are there volcanoes on the island of Hawaii?

Salvatore came home from the library with three books. Read the information he found and help him complete his notes and outline.

Island Geography

The Hawaiian Islands are a chain of islands located in the Pacific Ocean 2,000 miles from California. There are eight large islands and many small ones. The islands were formed by ancient volcanoes.

Hawaii is the youngest and largest of the islands. It's about 500,000 years old. Kauai, the oldest, is about 6 million years old.

Hawaii

The Hawaiian Islands are made up of 8 large islands and 124 small islands and reefs. The islands were formed by the lava flow from volcanoes.

There are five volcanoes on the island of Hawaii. Two of the volcanoes, Mauna Loa and Kilauea, are active. Kilauea is located on the southeastern edge of Hawaii Volcanoes National Park. Mauna Loa can be seen in the northwestern section of the same park.

Name:

Using Several References 2

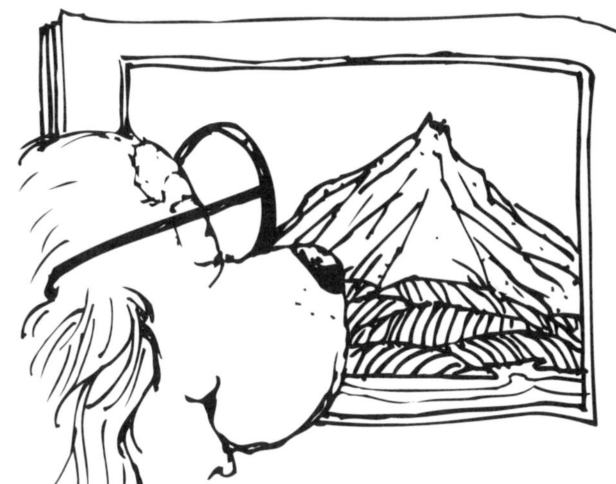

Hawaii's Tall Volcano

Mauna Kea on the island of Hawaii is the world's highest volcano. It rises 33,476 feet from the bottom of the ocean floor. It doesn't look as tall as it really is. Only 13,796 feet of Mauna Kea is above sea level. There are pockets of snow near the top or summit.

Here are Salvatore's notes. His mother called him to dinner before he finished writing details about Mauna Kea.

 **Finish the notes for him.**

Why is Hawaii called "The Big Island"?
  largest of 8 large islands
Are there volcanoes on the island of Hawaii?
  five volcanoes on Hawaii
  Mauna Loa and Kilauea are active
  Kilauea is on southeastern edge of Hawaii
    Volcanoes National Park
  Mauna Loa is on northwestern side of the park
  Mauna Kea is the world's highest volcano

____

____

____

Name:

Using Several References 3

Use the notes to complete Salvatore's outline.

The Island of Hawaii

I. Biggest of the Hawaiian Islands

II. Volcanoes on the island

A. Kilauea

1. active

2. southeastern edge of Hawaii Volcanoes National Park

B. Mauna Loa

1. ____________________

2. northwestern side of Hawaii Volcanoes National Park

C. Mauna Kea

1. ____________________

2. ____________________

3. ____________________

4. ____________________

Your Review Guide

The following list is a review of different ways to remember and write about nonfiction. You can use the list as a guide when you need to write a report or find information for a school project.

1. Before you read, write questions about what you want to know.
2. Read. Write the main ideas. (You can use the answers to the questions as the main ideas, or use the main ideas of the paragraphs you read.)
3. Map the main ideas under the topic or title.
4. Write the important details that tell about the main ideas.
5. Map the details under the main ideas.
6. Using the map, write an outline. The map and outline put the information in order so that you can tell or write about what you have read.

Important Reminder

It's important not to copy information from a book word for word. Many stories are copyrighted. That means the person who wrote the article or the publisher who printed it owns the story. An outline helps you write information in your own words.

Every person has a special way of telling a story. It's important that you share your story your way.

Name:

Outline Form

____

I. ______________________

A. ______________________

B. ______________________

C. ______________________

II. ______________________

A. ______________________

B. ______________________

C. ______________________

III. ______________________

A. ______________________

B. ______________________

C. ______________________

IV. ______________________

A. ______________________

B. ______________________

C. ______________________

Evaluating Information

Students display critical evaluation of reading material when they draw conclusions, generalize, summarize, or change the material to a new form.

ACTIVITIES

It Doesn't Belong (Page 124)
An important part of finding information is being able to recognize extraneous detail. This activity provides practice with this skill.

Drawing Conclusions (Pages 125–127)
Students read about what the skill of drawing conclusions involves and then practice it.

Summarizing What You Read (Pages 128 and 129)
Being able to summarize succinctly what is read is a difficult skill. These pages provide practice exercises.

Learning to Generalize (Pages 130 and 131)
Generalizing takes drawing a conclusion a step further—to forming an opinion about a whole group of people, animals, events, or places.

Transforming an Article into a Picture, Chart, or Poem (Pages 132–137)
Students practice transforming information into a map and an outline. These pages provide practice in changing information into three new forms.

Name:

It Doesn't Belong

Sometimes the details you read are interesting, but they don't fit under your main ideas or answer questions about your subject. Here are two exercises to help you eliminate information that does not fit under the main ideas.

Decide which of the facts below fit under the main idea, Parts of a Leaf. Cross out the details that don't belong.

Parts of a Leaf

- a blade is the broad, flat part of the leaf
- roots are another part of the plant
- the stem of the leaf is called the petiole
- a bulb is an underground stem
- leaves have many sizes and shapes
- tubes or veins in the leaf carry water and dissolved mineral food
- other tubes take food away from the leaf
- the midrib is the middle of the leaf

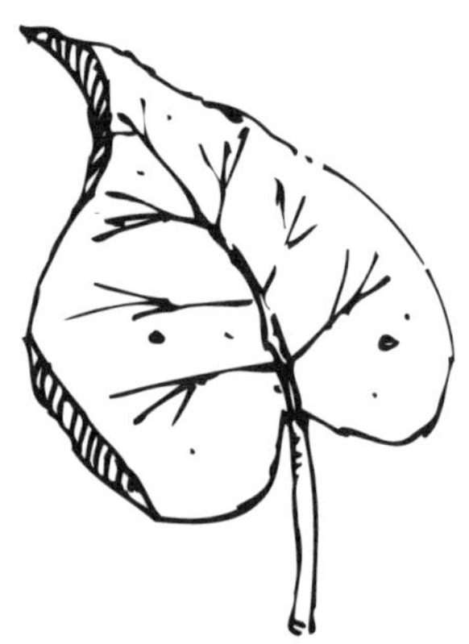

Help Sidney Student edit his report about the octopus. Draw a line through the information in the article that doesn't tell about the octopus.

The Octopus

The octopus lives in the sea. It's a member of the mollusk family, but it doesn't have shell armor to protect its body. Clams are mollusks that have two shells. The octopus has no backbone. Its mouth has a horny beak. Many sea animals can be found on the ocean floor. The octopus has eight tentacles with suction-cup disks that can grip its prey. Its relative the squid has ten tentacles. Some, like the Pacific octopus, grow up to 30 feet in diameter. Others are only two to three inches across. Slugs are an example of land mollusks.

Using its beak, the octopus can crush the shells of lobsters and crabs for a seafood dinner. It can wiggle a tentacle so it looks like a tasty worm. Curious fish that swim by to take a look end up inside the octopus. The shipworm is a mollusk with a different menu. It eats into the wood on piers and boats.

When threatened, the octopus lets off a dark, cloudy liquid and jets away. Squids shoot out a dark liquid too. A soft body allows the octopus to squeeze into small spaces between rocks. The rocks in the sea also serve as hideouts for the moray eel. There the octopus is safe from other sea creatures looking for a soft meal.

The octopus can see trouble coming. It has good eyesight, even in deep water. For more protection, this clever sea creature can change color to blend in with its ocean hideaway. Squids often swim in large schools for protection.

Drawing Conclusions

Thinking about what you read is just as important as finding facts in a story. Sometimes the information you read does not answer your question directly, but you can figure out the answer by putting together "clues" from the story. This is called **drawing conclusions**. Here is an example:

You are trying to find out which place in the United States has recorded the hottest temperature. In the Almanac you read:

> The world temperature record is held by El Azizia, Libya. On September 13, 1922, the recorded temperature was 136°F. Death Valley, California, registered the second highest temperature of 134°F in July 1913.

You can draw a conclusion from these facts:

If the country of Libya holds the world's first-place record and Death Valley in the United States the second, no other place in the United States would have a higher temperature. Therefore, even though it doesn't say that Death Valley has the highest recorded temperature in the United States, you know no other place has recorded a higher temperature.

From the information you conclude that the highest recorded temperature in the United States was in Death Valley.

Name:

Drawing Conclusions 2

Read the following stories. At the end of the first two selections, make an X in front of the conclusion that can be made from the information in the story. For the third selection, you will write your own conclusion.

The Flat-Headed Frog

The flat-headed frog lives in the Australian desert. When water is available, it absorbs water through its skin. It drinks large quantities of water when it can. The frog's body swells to resemble a round ball when filled with water. During the dry season when it's very hot, the frog, bloated with water, tunnels under the ground to stay cool.

_____ The flat-headed frog can survive without water for long periods of time.

_____ The flat-headed frog drinks too much water.

School Daze

Thursday after school, Alice watched two movies on TV. Her science report on spiders was due the next day. She didn't worry because she had written half of it on Tuesday. She planned to finish the rest of the report the next morning before she went to school. Accidentally, Alice set her alarm for 6:00 p.m. instead of 6:00 a.m. She didn't wake up until 7:15 a.m. She had 30 minutes to get ready for school and eat breakfast.

_____ Alice didn't have enough time to finish her science report Friday morning.

_____ Reports about birds are more interesting than spider reports.

Manatees

The manatee is an endangered animal. Sometimes known as the seacow, this gentle animal does not harm others. Many manatees are killed or seriously injured when they are hit by motorboats. Laws limit the use of motorboats in areas where manatees can be found, but accidents continue to happen.

The manatee feeds on seagrass along the coast and near rivers. Many people have moved to Florida and crowded into areas where manatees live. Some of the feeding areas are destroyed when houses and businesses are built along the shore. Today there are about 2,000 manatees living along the coastal areas of the United States.

Conclusion: ____

____

____

Name:

Drawing Conclusions 3

Read the following story about Jane Addams, a pioneer in caring for the poor. At the end of the story, write a conclusion about her work that is not given in the story.

Jane Addams 1860–1935

Jane Addams opened a settlement house in Chicago to help poor people. Many were immigrants who had come from other countries. The house was called Hull House.

Jane came from a wealthy family, but she suffered from a crooked back as a child. She felt ugly and was unable to do many things other children could do. She decided to help others when she grew up.

At Hull House she helped mothers learn better ways to care for their children. She aided the sick and helped people find decent places to live. She showed them how to cook nourishing foods.

Jane and her friend Ellen Starr set up an art gallery and provided books and magazines for people who visited Hull House. They felt that poor people who worked long hours under poor conditions should enjoy beauty. The art and reading rooms were a great success. They added a music school. There was a room for older members of the family to work on crafts. They made carvings and sewn items they could sell for money.

Jane set up a playground for children so they wouldn't have to play in the streets. There was a nursery school where working mothers could leave their children during the day.

____

____

____

____

____

____

Name:

Summarizing What You Read

Do you ever read a TV magazine or newspaper to see what a program is going to be about? Have you read what a book jacket says a story is about before deciding to check out the book? Both of these are examples of **summaries.**

A summary tells the most important ideas of an article or a story in a very brief way. Even when you are reading for fun, try to summarize what you have read.

Read the following two paragraphs. Ask yourself, "What is the paragraph about?" For each paragraph, choose the sentence that you think best summarizes the information.

Spider Webs

Each kind of spider has a special web shape. Orb weavers spin round webs. Grass spiders build webs that are shaped like funnels. A purse-web spider spins a long tube. A comb-footed spider builds a hanging bell-shaped web. These special webs are used to trap insects. Some also serve as homes for the spider.

_____ Spider webs trap insects.
_____ Spider webs come in many shapes and uses.
_____ Grass spiders build funnel-shaped webs.

Central Park

Five hundred people attended the opening of the new park in Central City. The lake was ready for canoes and kayaks. There are two play areas, one for young children and another with twisting slides and tunnels for older children. Green trees, grass, and a small stream with several families of ducks will attract weekend crowds with picnic lunches.

The mayor cut the ribbon for the new park. In his speech he said, "This beautiful park is for everyone in Central City. Children will have a place to play, and families can enjoy time outdoors together."

After his speech the mayor and the city workers who built the park jogged the two miles around the lake.

_____ Central Park offers many choices for recreational activities.
_____ Central Park was created recently.
_____ Children will have a lot to do in Central Park.

Name:

Summarizing What You Read 2

Sally Student was trying to decide if she wanted to spend the money to see the movie *Go West Young Spaniel.* She knew that Samantha had seen it, so she asked Samantha to tell her about the story. Forty-five minutes later, Sally had heard every detail of the movie and was bored to tears. Poor Samantha—no one ever taught her how to summarize!

How are your summarizing skills? Read the following selections and follow the instructions.

Alberta, Canada

There are many scenic places for tourists to see in Alberta, Canada. The Rocky Mountains, many national parks, and wilderness areas are visited by millions of people every year. Banff National Park is a favorite tourist stop. Dinosaur Provincial Park and the Royal Tyrrell Museum draw many visitors who want to know more about these fascinating prehistoric animals.

Write a slogan for a travel advertisement that summarizes the paragraph.

____

____

____

Venus's-Flytrap

A very strange plant grows in North Carolina. It eats insects! It is called Venus's-flytrap because it traps insects. There is not enough food in the soil where this plant grows, so the flytrap catches insects to eat.

This strange plant has leaves that work like a steel trap. The two halves of the leaf are hinged in the middle. When an insect lands on it, the leaf closes and traps the insect. Juices in the plant digest the insect.

Write a summary of no more than two sentences.

____

____

____

____

Name:

Learning to Generalize

When you **generalize**, you form an opinion about the information you have read. Often that opinion, or general statement, is about a whole group of people, animals, events, or places. Here are some examples from selections you have read:

After reading about spiders you could generalize that spiders spend a lot of time weaving webs.

When you read about Alberta, Canada, you could make the general statement that Alberta is a good place for tourists to visit.

When you read the story "School Daze," you could generalize that it's better to finish homework before watching TV.

Read the following paragraph about monkeys.

Choose the statement that a person could generalize after reading the paragraph.

Monkeys are very nosy and lively. They like to learn how things are made. They will often take things apart. A monkey can't resist finding out what is inside a package. Monkeys like to swing and jump from place to place. They need lots of space to climb.

_____ Monkeys are fun to watch.
_____ Monkeys would make a mess in your kitchen.
_____ A monkey would not make a good pet.

Beginning below are three stories about the marsh mosquito. Even though just facts are used, each paragraph presents a different opinion about the mosquito.

Read each paragraph.

Write a generalization for each paragraph.

The Marsh Mosquito

The Anderson Marsh is a breeding ground for mosquitoes. The large marsh mosquitoes are attacking animals and people in the nearby community of Andersonville. The mosquitoes carry diseases and cause great discomfort. The city council will vote on Tuesday on whether to drain the marsh and rid the city of this pest.

Generalization: ____

____

Name:

Learning to Generalize 2

The Marsh Mosquito

Many birds that call Anderson Marsh home depend on the marsh mosquito larvae for their food. Each year they visit the marsh and build their nests. They feed themselves and their young on small insects and larvae found in the marsh. The frogs, toads, and fish in the marsh also depend on the larvae for food.

Generalization: ______________________________

____

Mosquito Control

Many mosquitoes in Andersonville do not come from the marsh. Gardeners save rainwater in barrels and jugs for their gardens. Large numbers of mosquitoes are breeding in the open water containers.

Generalization: ______________________________

____

Notice that the information a writer includes in a story can change the way a reader thinks about a subject. Writers can change your ideas by including some facts and leaving out others. It's important to read more than one story about a subject before you form an opinion or generalize.

Write one general statement about mosquitoes that is based on the information in all three stories.

____

____

____

Name:

Transforming an Article into a Picture

When you made an information map or outline from the facts in a story, you **transformed** or changed the form of what you read.

There are many ways to transform information.

 **You can picture facts. You can show the stages of a frog's life cycle with pictures.**

 **You can make a chart that is easily understood.**

Butterfly Metamorphosis

 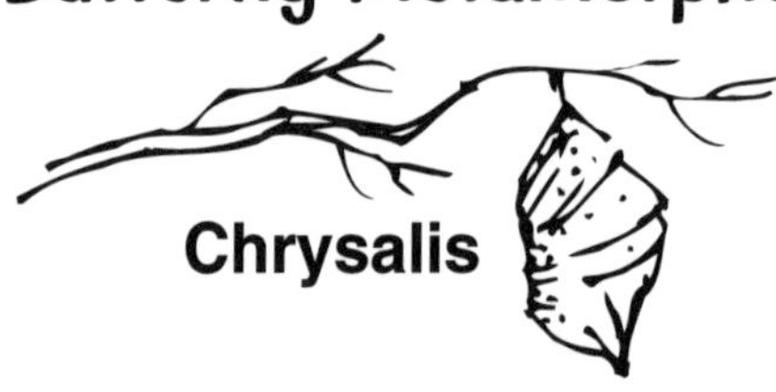 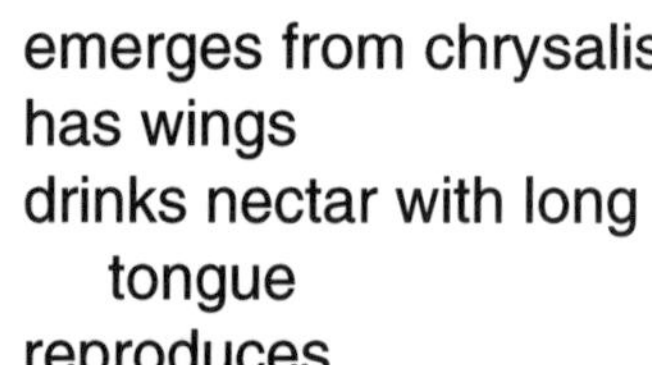

Larva	Chrysalis	Adult
hatches from egg wormlike eats constantly	spun from silk turns hard attaches to a stem	emerges from chrysalis has wings drinks nectar with long tongue reproduces

 **You can include the information in a poem or poster. The following poem is from the information on spiders. Draw spider pictures around the poem.**

Spider Webs

Round, funnel, tubes, and bell—
The spider weaves a magic spell.
A place to stay,
A net for prey,
The spider's web serves very well.

Evaluating Information

Name:

Transforming an Article into a Picture 2

Articles that tell you the steps of a process are good ones to transform into pictures. In fact, this is often the clearest way to communicate a process to your audience.

- **Read this selection about how bread is made.**
- **Decide on the six most important ideas to show.**
- **Draw the six ideas in the boxes below.**

Wheat, harvested by machines, is taken to mills to be ground into flour. Bakeries purchase large bags of flour from the flour mills. At the bakery, ingredients such as flour, salt, sugar, yeast, water, and eggs are blended together in large mixers. The dough is shaped into loaves and left to rise before baking. After baking, the fresh bread is wrapped and sent to the store. Now you can fix your favorite sandwich.

Name:

Transforming an Article into a Chart

Sidney Student decided to take his report and display the information in chart form. He left out a few details. Read Sidney's report again and add details to the chart. The numbers in parentheses tell you how many details to add.

The Octopus

The octopus lives in the sea. It's a member of the mollusk family, but it doesn't have shell armor to protect its body. The octopus has no backbone. Its mouth has a horny beak. The octopus has eight tentacles with suction-cup disks that can grip its prey. Some, like the Pacific octopus, grow up to 30 feet in diameter. Others are only two to three inches across.

Using its beak, the octopus can crush the shells of lobsters and crabs for a seafood dinner. It can wiggle a tentacle so it looks like a tasty worm. Curious fish that swim by to take a look end up inside the octopus.

When threatened, the octopus lets off a dark, cloudy liquid and jets away. A soft body allows the octopus to squeeze into small spaces between rocks. There the octopus is safe from other sea creatures looking for a soft meal.

The octopus can see trouble coming. It has good eyesight, even in deep water. For more protection, this clever sea creature can change color to blend in with its ocean hideaway.

The Octopus

Protection (1)	Body (2)	Food (1)	Size (1)
lets off dark liquid before escaping soft body squeezes into tight spaces good eyesight spots trouble	soft no backbone suction disks	beak crushes shells of lobsters and crabs for seafood meal	some only two to three inches in diameter

Name:

A Charting Challenge

Get together with one to three classmates. Choose a sport you enjoy watching or playing.

On the form below, make a chart for the sport. Suggested column headings are *Equipment, Players, Scoring, General Rules*. You may add more columns or remove any columns from this list.

Name of Sport			

Chart Form

Name:

Transforming an Article into a Poem

Read the following paragraphs about the sun. Using some of the information in the story, write a poem about the sun.

Here are some ideas to help you:

- Form a picture in your mind about the sun and use a word to communicate what you "see."
- Your poem does not have to rhyme.
- If you have learned to write cinquain verse, you might use that form.
- Include several facts.
- Use words that are pleasing to the ear.

The Sun

The sun is our closest star. The sun is made up of gasses. The temperature on the surface of the sun is about 5,800 degrees Centigrade. Anything coming close to the sun would burn up from the heat.

Atomic particles, light, and radio waves are let off by the sun. Most ultraviolet light from the sun is filtered out in the atmosphere before it reaches the earth. Ultraviolet light can be used to kill germs, but too much of it can harm animals and plants.

Solar heat affects the climate and oceans on earth. Heat from the sun evaporates water into the air. About 500 trillion tons of water on earth evaporate every year. When the water falls back on the earth, it helps plants grow. Heat from the sun heats the air. Winds develop from the movement of cool and warm air. Currents in the ocean are caused by solar heat.

Most plants need sunlight to grow. Plants change carbon dioxide and sunlight into sugar and starch. This solar-made food helps the plants grow the leaves and fruit that we eat.

____

____

____

____

____

____

Reading Nonfiction Skills Checklist ✓

	Students' Names									
Uses prereading questions to locate important facts when reading about: events										
animals										
biographies										
Uses a traditional or electronic card catalog to locate information in the library										
Uses a table of contents and index to locate specific information										
Uses key words to scan for information										
Creates an information map using main ideas and details										
Takes notes using only necessary words										
Creates a simple outline of main ideas and details from notes or an information map										
Recognizes extraneous detail in an information article										
Puts events in chronological order										
Draws logical conclusions from information read										
Summarizes information read										
Generalizes to form an opinion about information read										
Reports information using a variety of forms: pictures										
poem										
chart										
Shows interest in learning new reading skills for accessing information										
Shows interest in reading nonfiction for own purposes										

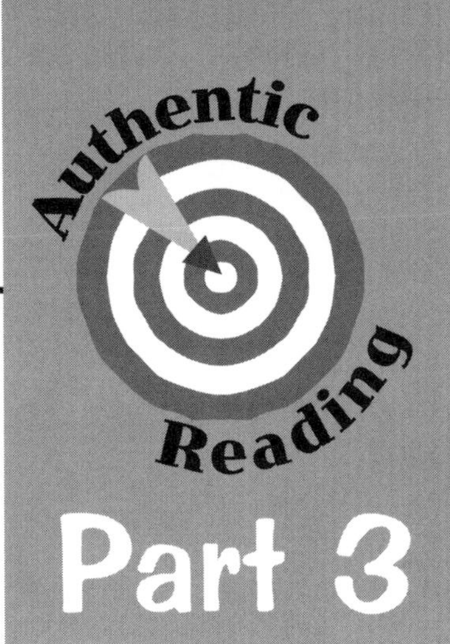

Reading Reference Materials

The activities in this section provide practice in using three common reference resources:

- Dictionary
- Encyclopedia
- Atlas

Room Environment

In one corner of your classroom, set up a small library or special reading area. This area should include the reference books described below on easily accessed shelves, one or two tables with reading lamps, or even a couch, rug, or beanbag chair for comfort. Small note pads and pencils for community use might also be helpful.

Dictionaries

Ideally, your classroom should be furnished with enough dictionaries for each student to have access to one. They do not all have to be alike; in fact, it is an asset to have a variety of dictionaries. Be sure that you have at least one collegiate level or unabridged dictionary on hand.

Encyclopedias

All of the encyclopedia work can be accomplished with just one set of encyclopedias in the room, but two or more sets are preferable. Again, variety is an asset here. Where the explorations call for specific information, the topics chosen are not easily dated, so that the older encyclopedias you might have should work just fine. Of course, if you have access to a continually updated online encyclopedia, so much the better!

Atlases

Atlases should be as current as possible, as political changes in the world make the old ones obsolete. Again, it is ideal to have one book for each child, but the activities may be done with partners or small groups if there are not enough books to go around.

Many of the explorations for reference materials can be adapted to the cooperative group format. Activities that lend themselves particularly well to group work are described in each section.

Most of the explorations require nothing more than the reference books, paper, and pencil. Where additional materials are needed, they are listed in the explanation of the activity.

Dictionary Dynamics

Students need to know how to use a dictionary to locate word meanings and spellings quickly and accurately. The pages that follow provide an opportunity for students to become acquainted with the parts of a dictionary entry and to get important hands-on dictionary practice.

ACTIVITIES

The Parts of a Dictionary Entry (Pages 143 and 144)

To review what each part of a dictionary entry represents, reproduce page 143 onto an overhead transparency and reproduce a copy of page 144 for each student. You may choose to do the whole page together, or to review the parts and then have students number the parts independently.

Guide Words (Pages 145 and 146)

Have students work independently or with a partner to locate guide words in the dictionary. Begin by giving a pair of guide words to see how quickly students can find the correct page. Then give a word and ask students to use guide words to find it in the dictionary.

After reviewing the function of guide words, have students complete pages 145 and 146.

Using the Pronunciation Key (Page 147)

Review the sounds and symbols shown in the pronunciation key at the top of the page. Students are to read each word and then draw a picture to show what it says. (Students need to be aware that different markings and symbols are used in different dictionaries. This key may differ from those in students' class dictionaries and the indexes in their textbooks.)

Activities continued on Page 142

More Than One Meaning (Page 148)
Read the definitions for the word *fly.* Then write the number of the correct meaning for *fly* in each sentence.

Pages 149–171 contain five types of motivating activities that provide hands-on practice using a dictionary. Although exercises are grouped by type, it is suggested that you mix up the activities rather than doing an entire section at a time. These are ideal activities for partners or small groups. Once students are familiar with the formats, you may wish to use these activities as center activities.

Picture Dictionary (Pages 149–151)
Students look up each word and then draw a picture that clearly illustrates its meaning. Students are challenged not only to locate the word, but to demonstrate their understanding of the definition through their drawings. As a means of checking these pages, divide the class into groups to discuss the words and evaluate each other's responses.

Matching (Pages 152–156)
Students match the names of objects with the people or animals who might use those objects. To do this, students locate each word in the dictionary and find the definition that makes the most sense in the context given.

Categories (Pages 157–161)
Students look up unfamiliar words in the dictionary, read the definitions, and then determine in which of the given categories the word should be placed. Students must study all the definitions of the word to be certain they have found the best fit.

Label It! (Pages 162–166)
"Label It!" stimulates thinking abilities. Students must look up each word in the dictionary, determine its meaning, and then label the part of the picture that shows the word. Sometimes a word may describe more than one part of the picture, so students must stay alert to multiple meanings.

Spelling Sleuth (Pages 167–171)
"Spelling Sleuth" activities use the dictionary to locate the correct spelling of a given word. The words selected for these activities were taken from lists of frequently misspelled words. Students select the correct spelling from three choices. Often two of the choices may actually spell a word, so students must also read the definitions carefully to make sure that their choices are correct.

The Parts of a Dictionary Entry

1. **Entry Word**
The entry word is printed in bold type. It shows how the word is spelled and how it is divided into syllables.

2. **Small Raised Number**
The small raised number following the entry word is used when two or more entry words have the same spelling.

3. **Pronunciation**
The guide to how to pronounce the entry word is enclosed in parentheses. Each letter or other symbol stands for a certain sound. These symbols are explained in the pronunciation key.

4. **Definition**
The definition gives the meaning of the word. If there are multiple meanings for the word, each meaning is given a number.

5. **Sentence or Phrase**
Often a sentence or phrase is given to show how the word may be used. These are written in slanted (italic) letters.

6. **Part of Speech**
The part of speech is given for the entry word. When the word is used as more than one part of speech, definition numbers are printed before each part-of-speech label. The part of speech is written in slanted (italic) letters.

7. **Word Endings and Special Forms**
Word endings and special forms of words are written in bold letters.

8. **Word History**
The history of a word tells what language the English word came from and what the word meant in that language. It appears in square brackets.

9. **Idioms**
An idiom consists of a combination of words that cannot be understood from the meaning of the individual words. Idioms are printed in bold.

10. **Picture**
Sometimes a picture is given to show what a word means. There may also be a caption to give additional information.

Name:

The Parts of a Dictionary Entry 2

Use the numbers on page 143 to label the parts of each entry.

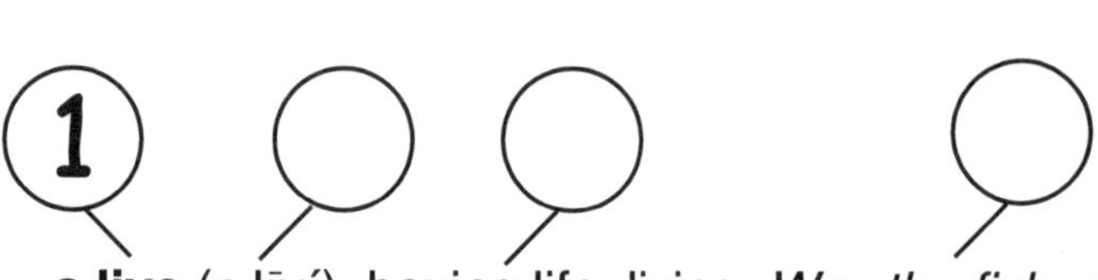

a live (ə līv´), having life; living; *Was the fish alive or dead? adjective.*

Look alive! Hurry up! Be quick!

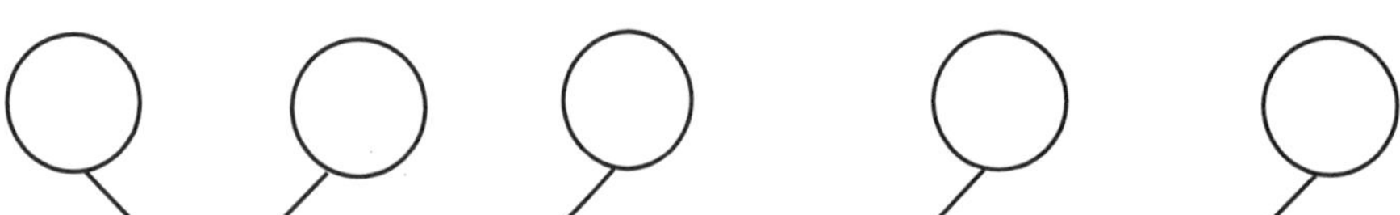

at las (at´ ləs), book of maps. *plural* **at las es**. [*Atlas* comes from the name of a giant in Greek myths who held up the sky on his shoulders. His picture appeared in early books of maps.]

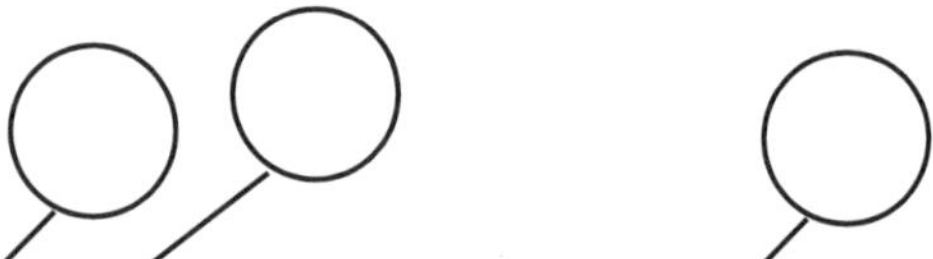

duck[1] (duk), **1** a swimming bird with a flat bill, short neck, short legs, and webbed feet. See picture. **2** a female duck. The male is called a drake. **3** the flesh of a duck used for food: *roast duck. noun.*

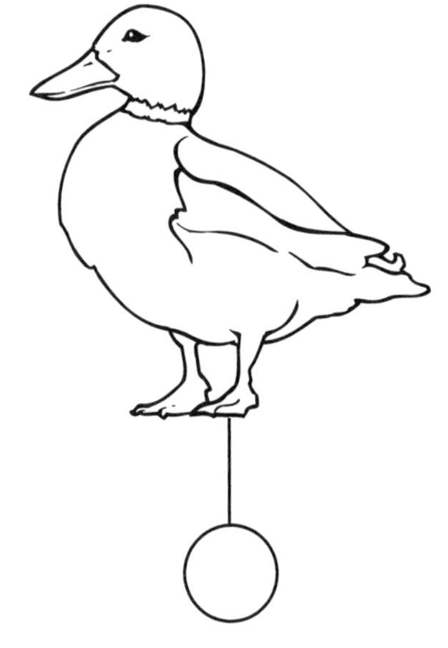

duck[2] (duk), **1** to plunge or dip under water and out again. **2** to lower the head or bend the body quickly to keep from being hit or seen: *The boy ducked to avoid a low branch. verb,*

ducked, ducking.

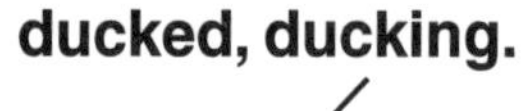

Name:

Guide Words 1

Guide words are found at the top of a dictionary page. Use guide words to help you find the word you are looking for more quickly.

The guide words are:	Circle the words that would be found on the page.		
1. cookie corn	carrot	coop	cord
	core	custard	copilot
	corduroy	climb	contest
2. gourd grasp	gown	grain	gopher
	graduate	grape	granny
	graze	gnaw	governor
3. peach pelt	pelican	peanut	peek
	parakeet	penguin	peck
	peculiar	pepper	peacock
4. tiger tiptoe	time	thunder	tomb
	tiny	tight	table
	tinfoil	tiptop	timber

Name:

Guide Words 2

Guide words are found at the top of a dictionary page. Use guide words to help you find the word you are looking for more quickly.

The guide words are:		Circle the words that would be found on the page.		
1. **bargain**	**basic**	barge barometer barrel	bashful basin batter	bassoon barrier basketball
2. **fifth**	**film**	fig figure fingernail	file final fight	finch fill filter
3. **monkey**	**moon**	moose moody monarch	monsoon more monopoly	monster Montana motor
4. **radio**	**rain**	rainbow rage raisin	ram radish rafter	raise rajah ragweed

Name:

Using the Pronunciation Key

a	**hat**	i	**it**	oi	**oil**	ch	**child**		**a** in about
ā	**age**	ī	**ice**	ou	**out**	ng	**long**		**e** in taken
ä	**father**	o	**hot**	u	**cup**	sh	**she**	ə =	**i** in pencil
e	**let**	ō	**open**	u̇	**put**	th	**thin**		**o** in lemon
ē	**equal**	ô	**order**	ü	**rule**	ŦH	**then**		**u** in circus
ėr	**term**					zh	**measure**		

Draw a picture of each word. Use the pronunciation key to help you read them.

pich´ ėr	häk	güs
ī´ brou	fä´ sit	süt´ kās
ôr´ inj	moŦHz	kə nü´

Name:

More Than One Meaning

Many words have more than one meaning. This dictionary entry gives 10 meanings for the word *fly*. Read the definitions and then write the number of the definition that fits the meaning of *fly* in the sentences below.

fly (flī), **1** move through the air with wings. **2** float or wave in the air. **3** cause to float or wave in the air. **4** travel in an aircraft. **5** pilot an aircraft. **6** carry by aircraft. **7** rush; move swiftly. **8** flap to cover buttons or a zipper on clothing. **9** baseball hit high in the air with a bat. **10** bat a baseball high in the air. **1–7, 10** *verb,* **flew, flown, flying**; **8, 9** *noun,* plural **flies**.

1. Some birds can fly long distances. ________
2. He flies airplanes for the army. ________
3. Our flag flies over the school every day. ________
4. He is going to fly to Florida for a vacation. ________
5. The fly ball sailed into the bleachers. ________
6. We flew packages to our cousin in Hawaii. ________
7. I flew to the table to catch the glass of milk before it spilled. ________
8. We are going to fly our kites after school lets out. ________

Write sentences showing the two remaining meanings of *fly*.

1. ____

2. ____

Name:

Picture Dictionary 1

Use a dictionary to find the definitions of the words on this page.

Draw a picture that clearly illustrates one meaning of the word in each box.

calamity	**germinate**
teal	**mince**
talisman	**peccary**

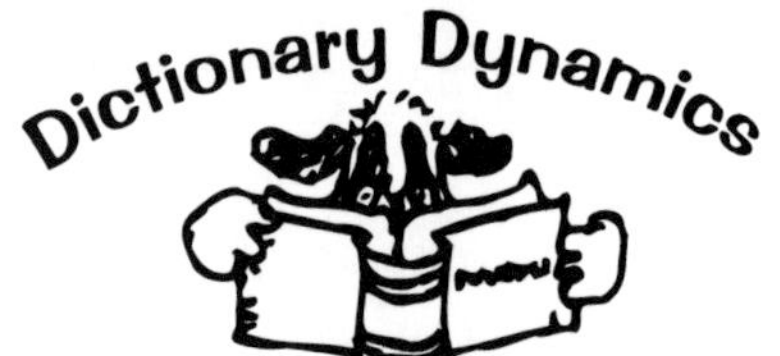

Name:

Picture Dictionary 2

- Use a dictionary to find the definitions of the words on this page.
- Draw a picture that clearly illustrates one meaning of the word in each box.

zither	tinge
sod	radiant
exuberant	wizened

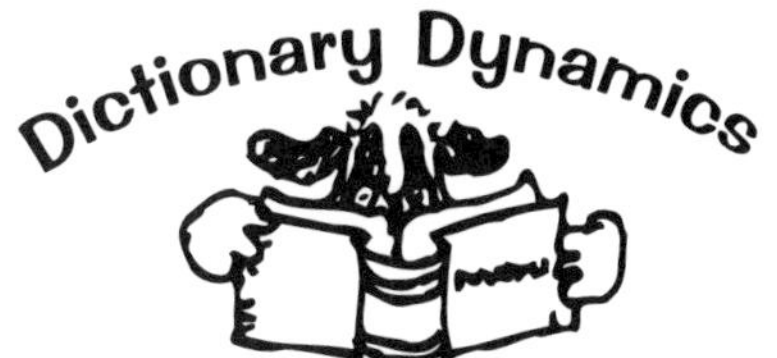

Name:

Picture Dictionary 3

Use a dictionary to find the definitions of the words on this page.

Draw a picture that clearly illustrates one meaning of the word in each box.

meringue	**palisade**
parapet	**morsel**
serrated	**pounce**

Name:

Matching 1

To complete each sentence, look up each word at the bottom of the page to determine which item belongs to each character and for information that will help you finish the sentence. Caution: Some of the words have more than one meaning, so read carefully!

1. A carpenter uses ____________________ to ______________________________.
2. A mechanic uses ____________________ to ______________________________.
3. A truck driver uses ____________________ to ______________________________.
4. A doctor uses ____________________ to ______________________________.
5. A writer uses ____________________ to ______________________________.
6. A baker uses ____________________ to ______________________________.
7. A lawyer uses ____________________ to ______________________________.
8. A fisherman uses ____________________ to ______________________________.

a brief	**a plane**
the clutch	**a spanner**
a creel	**leavening**
a pseudonym	**sutures**

Name:

Matching 2

To complete each sentence, look up each word at the bottom of the page to determine which item belongs to each character and for information that will help you finish the sentence. Caution: Some of the words have more than one meaning, so read carefully!

1. A bookkeeper uses ____________________ to ________________________________.
2. A wizard uses ____________________ to ________________________________.
3. A cowboy uses ____________________ to ________________________________.
4. A navigator uses ____________________ to ________________________________.
5. A pike uses ____________________ to ________________________________.
6. A glazier uses ____________________ to ________________________________.
7. A farmer uses ____________________ to ________________________________.
8. A king uses ____________________ to ________________________________.

a lariat	**a cistern**
a pane	**a scepter**
an incantation	**gills**
a sextant	**a ledger**

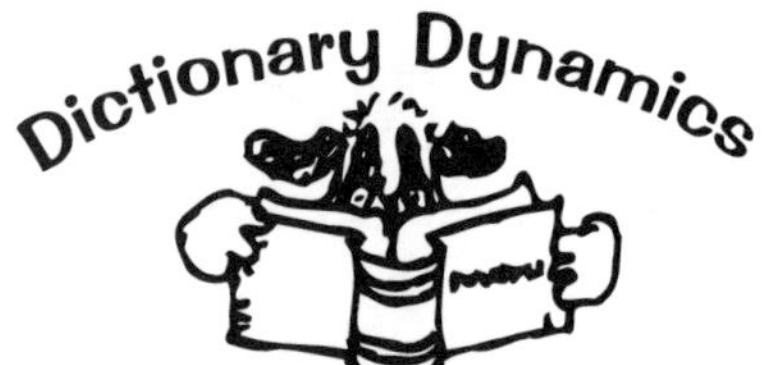

Name:

Matching 3

To complete each sentence, look up each word at the bottom of the page to determine which item belongs to each character and for information that will help you finish the sentence. Caution: Some of the words have more than one meaning, so read carefully!

1. A baby uses ____________________ to ________________________.
2. A sailor uses ____________________ to ________________________.
3. A conductor uses ________________ to ________________________.
4. A passenger uses ________________ to ________________________.
5. A gardener uses _________________ to ________________________.
6. A mason uses ___________________ to ________________________.
7. A farrier uses ___________________ to ________________________.
8. A rancher uses __________________ to ________________________.

an anvil	**a score**
a mast	**a dibble**
cement	**fescue**
a berth	**a bassinet**

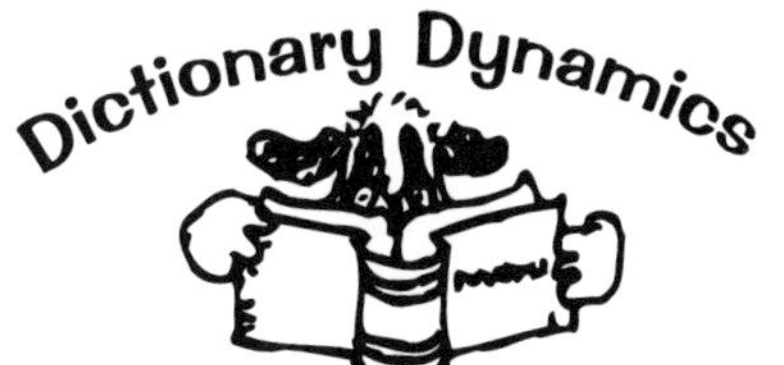

Name:

Matching 4

To complete each sentence, look up each word at the bottom of the page to determine which item belongs to each character and for information that will help you finish the sentence. Caution: Some of the words have more than one meaning, so read carefully!

1. A sculptor uses ____________________ to ___________________________.
2. A senator uses ____________________ to ___________________________.
3. A chef uses ____________________ to ___________________________.
4. A debater uses ____________________ to ___________________________.
5. An architect uses ____________________ to ___________________________.
6. A spider uses ____________________ to ___________________________.
7. An editor uses ____________________ to ___________________________.
8. A cellist uses ____________________ to ___________________________.

spinnerets	**a filibuster**
a bow	**a buttress**
an armature	**a rebuttal**
a roux	**a caret**

Name:

Matching 5

To complete each sentence, look up each word at the bottom of the page to determine which item belongs to each character and for information that will help you finish the sentence. Caution: Some of the words have more than one meaning, so read carefully!

1. A butcher uses ______________ to ______________.

2. A meteorologist uses ______________ to ______________.

3. A judge uses ______________ to ______________.

4. A falcon uses ______________ to ______________.

5. An barber uses ______________ to ______________.

6. An artist uses ______________ to ______________.

7. A seamstress uses ______________ to ______________.

8. An archer uses ______________ to ______________.

a gavel	**shears**
chambray	**a barometer**
a cleaver	**talons**
a quiver	**pigments**

Name:

Categories 1

Find the definition of each word at the bottom of the page. Write each word under the heading that makes the most sense.

How Many Legs?

No Legs

____
____
____
____
____

Two Legs

____
____
____
____
____

Four Legs

____
____
____
____
____

More Legs

____
____
____
____
____

executive	**anaconda**	**okapi**
hornet	**hyrax**	**centipede**
conger	**Gila monster**	**puffin**
dromedary	**scorpion**	**maggot**
tick	**mullet**	**arachnid**
newt	**hombre**	**grackle**
mandarin	**amoeba**	

Name:

Categories 2

Find the definition of each word at the bottom of the page. Write each word under the heading that makes the most sense.

What Should I Do With It?

Build It	Plant It
____________	____________
____________	____________
____________	____________
____________	____________
____________	____________

Eat It	Wear It
____________	____________
____________	____________
____________	____________
____________	____________
____________	____________

gauntlet	**palmetto**	**monocle**
pagoda	**beret**	**morsel**
sari	**minaret**	**buttress**
repast	**narcissus**	**flax**
tiara	**begonia**	**columbine**
spire	**turret**	**rusk**
ambrosia	**victuals**	

Name:

Categories 3

Find the definition of each word at the bottom of the page. Write each word under the heading that makes the most sense.

Let's Go Travel

Float

____
____
____
____
____
____
____

Roll

____
____
____
____
____
____
____

Fly

____
____
____

Slide

____
____
____

hansom	junk	sampan
dirigible	airship	ricksha
sulky	sledge	toboggan
sloop	kayak	perambulator
dory	glider	buggy
trolley	travois	skiff
jalopy	yawl	

Name:

Categories 4

Find the definition of each word at the bottom of the page. Write each word under the heading that makes the most sense.

Opposites

Noisy	Quiet
______	______
______	______
______	______
______	______
______	______

Hot	Cold
______	______
______	______
______	______
______	______
______	______

singe	**mute**	**sedate**
rime	**tropical**	**mime**
muffle	**bellow**	**magma**
tundra	**kiln**	**arctic**
calliope	**floe**	**clamor**
din	**forge**	**piccolo**
frigid	**stealthy**	

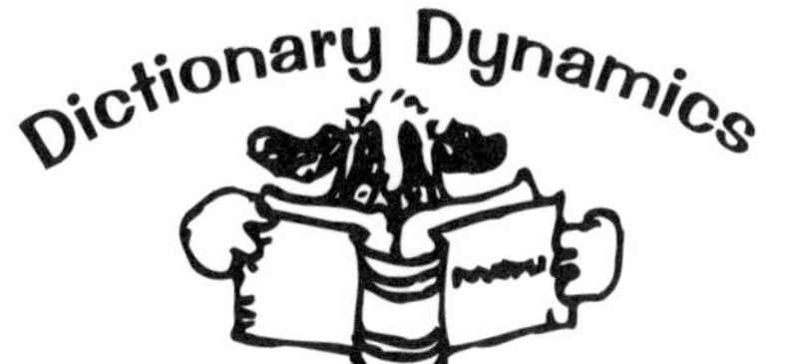

Name:

Categories 5

Find the definition of each word at the bottom of the page. Write each word under the heading that makes the most sense.

Animal Antics

Dog

____
____
____
____

Cat

____
____
____
____
____

Cow

____
____
____
____
____
____

Horse

____
____
____
____
____

lynx	**filly**	**dun**
dewlap	**cud**	**ruminant**
bovine	**canine**	**cur**
equine	**mongrel**	**tabby**
feline	**heifer**	**roan**
foal	**calico**	**low**
ocelot	**jackal**	

Name:

Label It! 1

Look up each word listed below. Write each word on the part of the picture where it belongs or draw a line from the word to the pictures. (Hint: Words may be used more than once.)

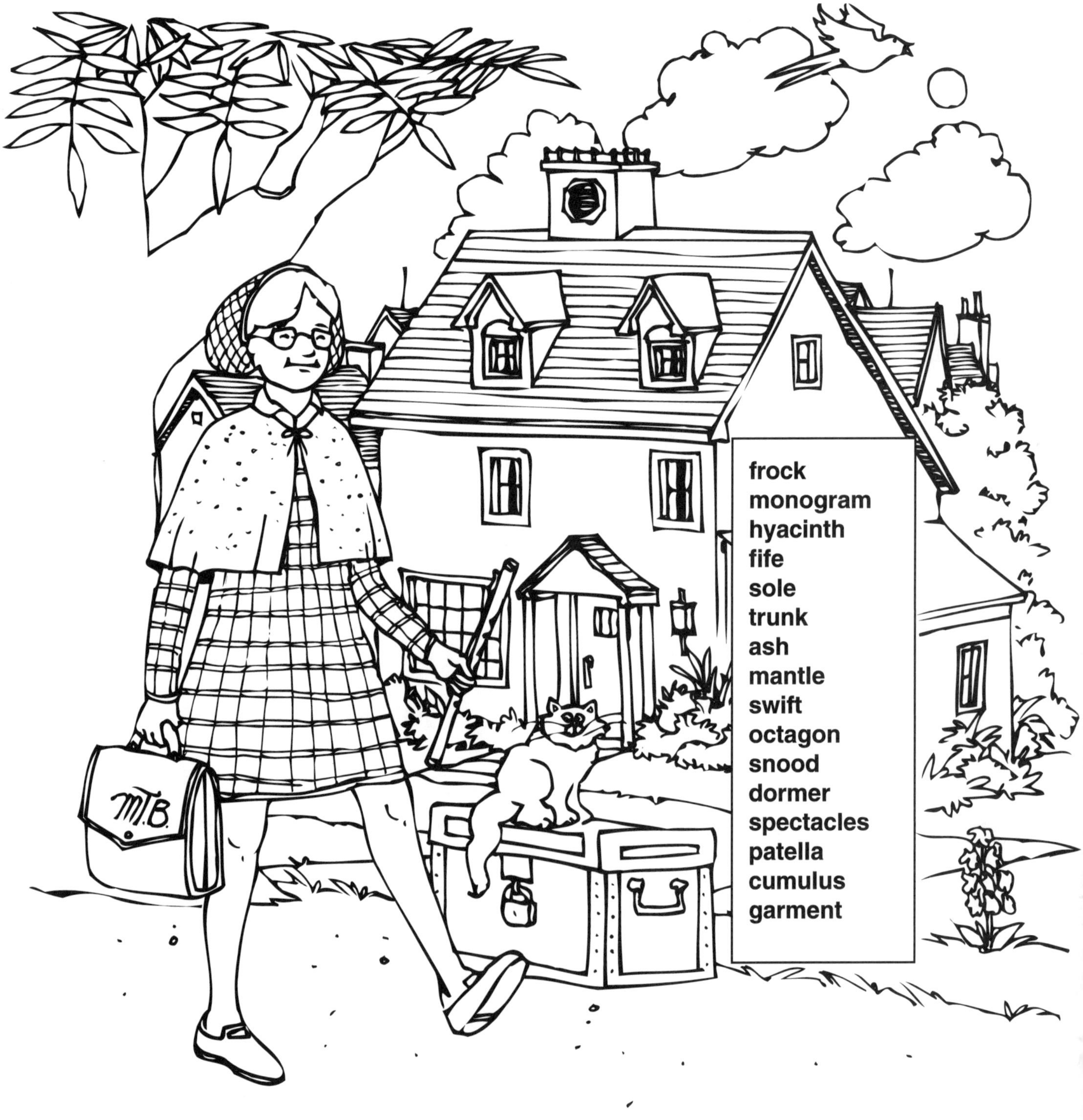

M.T.B.

frock
monogram
hyacinth
fife
sole
trunk
ash
mantle
swift
octagon
snood
dormer
spectacles
patella
cumulus
garment

Name:

Label It! 2

Look up each word listed below. Write each word on the part of the picture where it belongs or draw a line from the word to the picture.

rickety
proboscis
foyer
precipitation
belladonna
crone
cauldron
gargoyle
combustion
clapboard
specter
feline
rodent
vapor

Name:

Label It! 3

Look up each word listed below. Write each word on the part of the picture where it belongs or draw a line from the word to the picture.

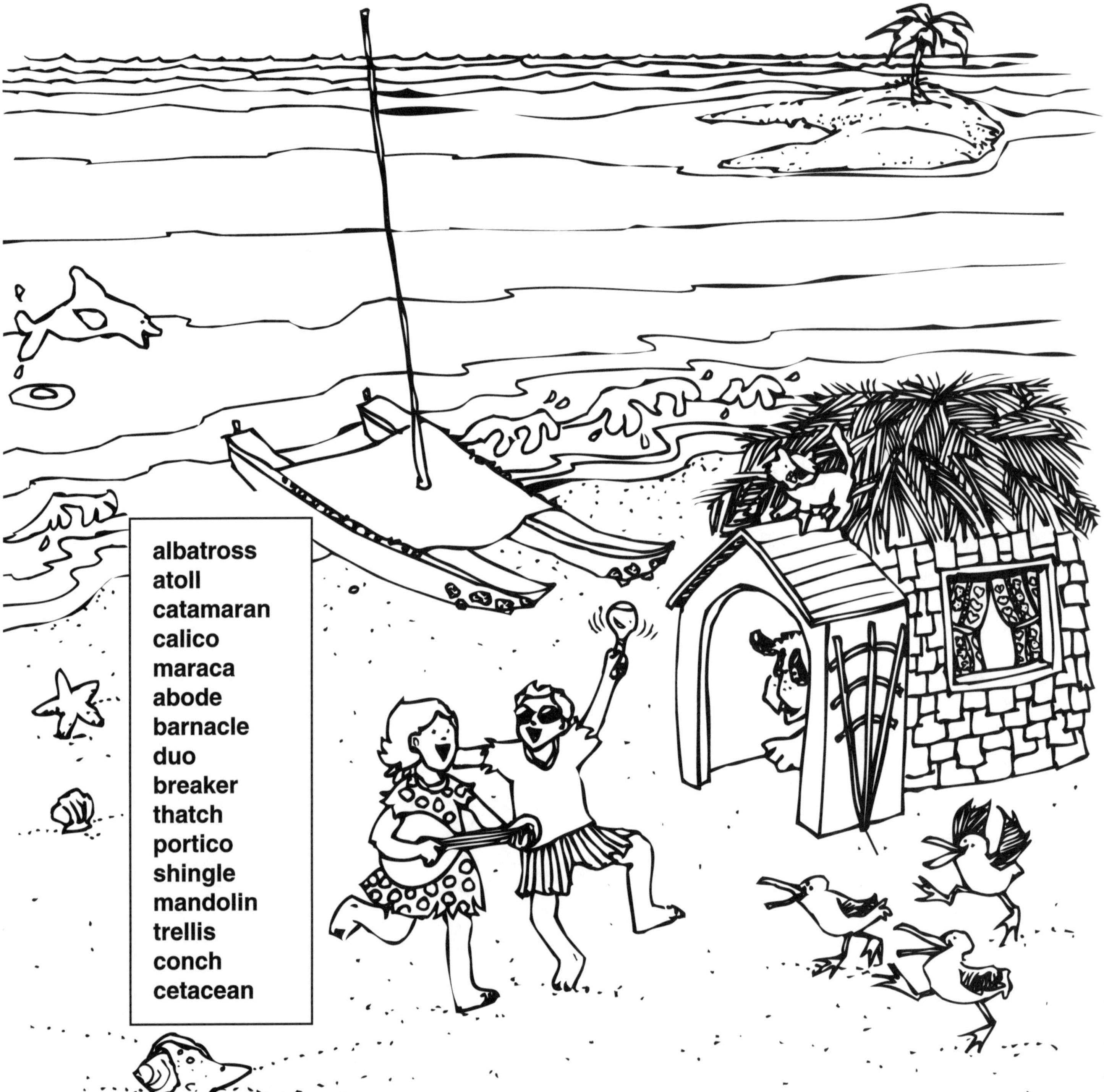

- albatross
- atoll
- catamaran
- calico
- maraca
- abode
- barnacle
- duo
- breaker
- thatch
- portico
- shingle
- mandolin
- trellis
- conch
- cetacean

Name:

Label It! 4

Look up each word listed below. Write each word on the part of the picture where it belongs or draw a line from the word to the picture.

crenellation
anvil
portcullis
monarch
farrier
Percheron
mail
scepter
gauntlet
archer
headstall
fetlock
pike
amethyst
moor
lobelia

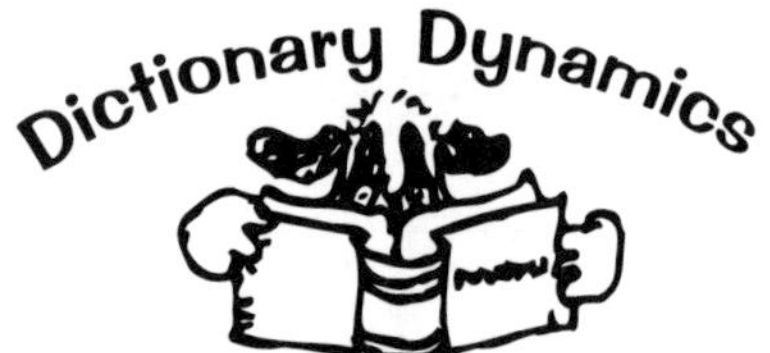

Name:

Label It! 5

Look up each word listed below. Write each word on the part of the picture where it belongs or draw a line from the word to the picture.

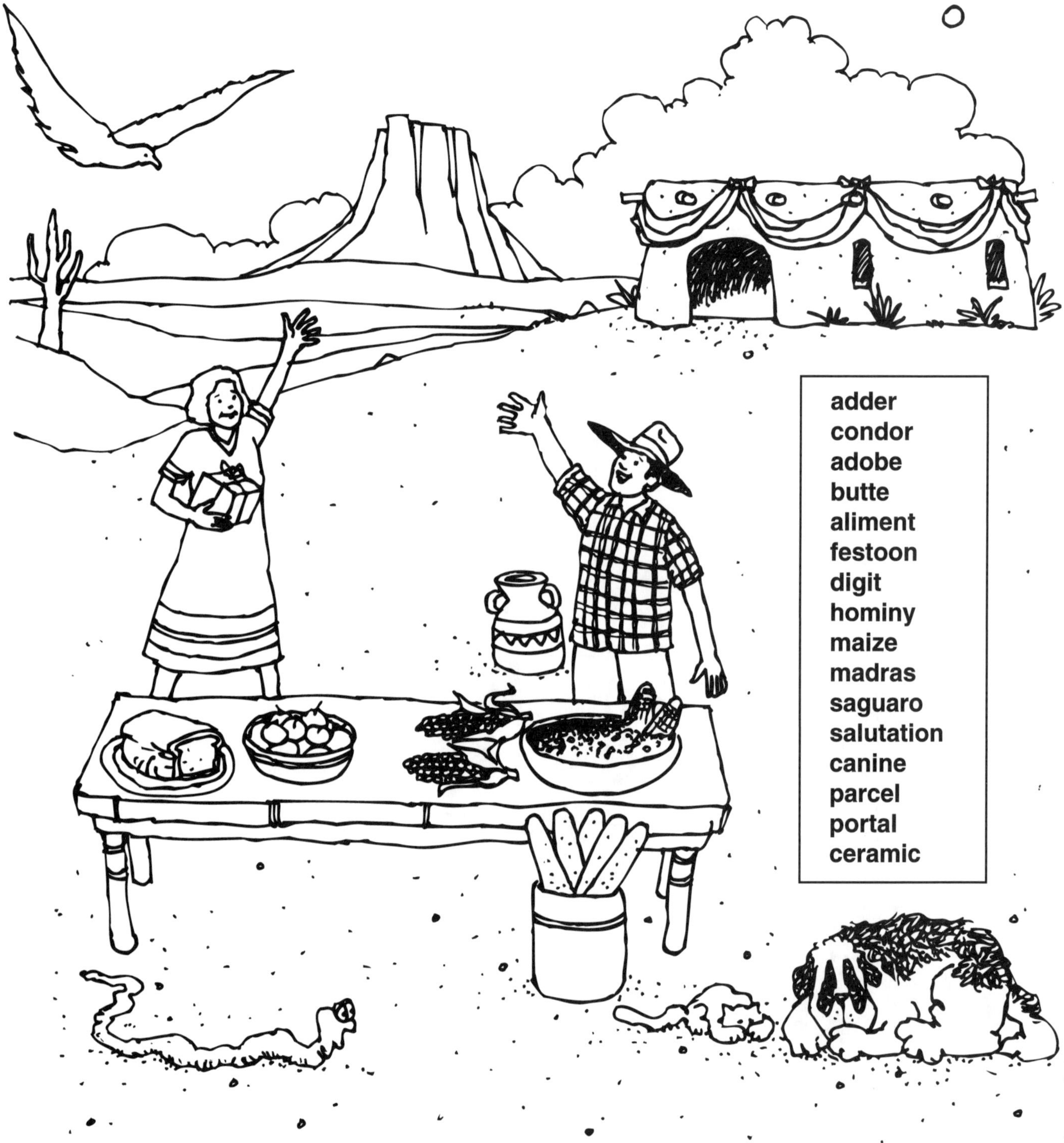

adder
condor
adobe
butte
aliment
festoon
digit
hominy
maize
madras
saguaro
salutation
canine
parcel
portal
ceramic

Name:

Spelling Sleuth 1

Using the list at the bottom of the page, choose the correct spelling for each numbered blank.

________ (1) Chip ________ (2) ________ (3)

(How to Make Everybody's ________ (4) ________ (5))

2 1/4 cups ________ (6)

1 teaspoon baking soda

1 teaspoon salt

1 cup butter or ________ (9)

3/4 cup ________ (7)

3/4 cup packed brown ________ (7)

1 teaspoon ________ (8) extract

2 eggs

2 cups ________ (1) chips

1 cup chopped nuts

Preheat oven to 375 degrees. In small bowl, combine ________ (6), baking soda, and salt. Set aside. In large bowl, combine butter, ________ (7), brown ________ (7), and ________ (8) extract. Beat until creamy. Beat in eggs. Gradually add ________ (6) mixture. Mix well. Stir in ________ (1) chips and nuts. Drop by rounded tablespoons onto ________ (2) sheets. (Do not ________ (10) the sheets.) Bake for 8 to 10 ________ (11). ________ (12)!

1. chalkolot, chocolate, chocklit
2. cookie, cooky, cookey
3. resipe, recipe, receipt
4. faverite, favorit, favorite
5. dessert, desert, dezert
6. flower, flour, flore
7. shuger, shugar, sugar
8. vinella, vanilla, vanila
9. margin, margarine, margerine
10. greece, grease, greace
11. minutes, minites, minnutes
12. dellicious, delishus, delicious

Name:

Spelling Sleuth 2

Using the list at the bottom of the page, choose the correct spelling for each numbered blank.

Mr. Snerdley ____________ (1) an Award

Ladies, Gentlemen, and all others present:

I cannot thank you ____________ (2) for the very great ____________ (3) you have bestowed upon me. I was ____________ (4) to receive the nomination, but never was I ____________ (5) enough to believe that I might ____________ (6) win the ____________ (7). I stand before you today as a ____________ (8) reminder that any ____________ (9) us can ____________ (10) so long as hard work and ____________ (11) are our watchwords. I would like to thank the ____________ (12) of the ____________ (13) that renewed my ____________ (14), ____________ (15) Popsnagle. I ____________ (16) that I will do my utmost to ____________ (17) your ____________ (18).

Thank you.

1. Excepts, Accepts, Acepts
2. enouff, ennough, enough
3. honnor, honer, honor
4. exited, excited, excitted
5. optomistic, optimistic, acoptamistic
6. actually, actualy, acctually
7. metal, mettle, medal
8. humble, humbel, hummble
9. amoung, among, ammong
10. suceed, succeed, succede
11. dedication, deddication, dedacation
12. cheif, chief, cheife
13. comittee, commitee, committee
14. lisence, license, liscence
15. Professor, Proffesor, Profesor
16. garauntee, guarentee, guarantee
17. excede, exceed, accede
18. expections, exppectations, expectations

Name:

Spelling Sleuth 3

Using the list at the bottom of the page, choose the correct spelling for each numbered blank.

Dear ______________________ (1),

On the ______________________ (2) of ______________________ (3)

I am ______________________ (4) a ______________________ (5)

__________________ (6) __________________ (7) the __________________ (8).

Please do not tell me that you think my plan is __________________ (9).

I have ______________________ (10) ______________________ (11)

to make the trip a ______________________ (12). My __________________ (13)

has told me that I could get ______________________ (14), but I am willing

to make that __________________ (15) in order to make __________________ (16).

I am full of ______________________ (17) and sure that I will be

______________________ (18).

______________________ (19),

Ramona

1. frend, freind, friend
2. eight, eighth, eigth
3. February, Februery, Febuary
4. begining, beggining, beginning
5. bicycle, bycicle, bicicle
6. expidition, expedition, expedision
7. across, accross, accrost
8. artic, arttic, arctic
9. rediculous, ridiculous, rediculuos
10. everthing, evereything, everything
11. necessery, necessary, neccesary
12. sucess, success, susess
13. docter, docktor, doctor
14. neumonia, pneumonia, newmonia
15. sacrifice, saccrifice, sacrafice
16. histry, history, histery
17. confidence, coffidence, confidense
18. alrite, allright, all right
19. Sincerely, Sincerly, Sincerlly

Name:

Spelling Sleuth 4

Using the list at the bottom of the page, choose the correct spelling for each numbered blank.

News ________________ (1)

For the ________ (2) night in a row, a ________ (3) has broken into a ________________ (4) ________________ (5) store. On each ________ (6) he has left ________ (7) bills to pay for the ________________ (8) he has stolen. The ________________ (9) of ________ (10) Gordon Hamilton has been arrested, but insists that he is ________ (11). Police have asked the crime ________ (12) to ________ (13) the fingerprints found at the ________ (14). The owner of the ________ (15) has told police that he will bear the ________ (16) of the investigation. There should be an ________________ (17) to this ________________ (18) any ________________ (19).

1. bullitin, buletin, bulletin
2. ninth, ningth, nineth
3. theif, thief, theef
4. neghborhood, neighberhood, neighborhood
5. jewlery, jewlry, jewelry
6. occasion, ocasion, occassion
7. conterfit, counterfeit, counterfit
8. gyms, jims, gems
9. shofar, chauffeur, chaufeur
10. milionaire, millionaire, millionair
11. innocent, inocent, innacent
12. laberatory, labrotory, laboratory
13. examine, examin, examen
14. seine, scene, seen
15. business, busyness, buisness
16. expence, expense, expanse
17. answer, anser, awnser
18. mistery, mystry, mystery
19. minite, minute, minnute

Name:

Spelling Sleuth 5

Using the list at the bottom of the page, choose the correct spelling for each numbered blank.

Dear ______________________ (1),

______________ (2) never ______________ (3) what ______________ (4)

today! Maria and I hid a rubber snake in Mr. Gumber's desk

______________ (5). When he ______________ (6) the ______________ (5)

he saw the snake and ______________ (7) ______________ (8)

out of his chair. He ______________ (9) to ______________ (10) that he

was ______________ (11), but he ______________ (12) keep

from ______________ (13) along with the rest of the class.

He did ______________ (14) that we will have to see Mrs. Fletcher,

the ______________ (15), ______________ (16). I hope she has

a good ______________ (17) of ______________ (18)!

Your Friend,

Brian

1. Dairy, Diary, Direy
2. You'll, Yule, Youll
3. gess, geuss, guess
4. hapened, happened, hapend
5. drauer, drawer, drore
6. opend, oppened, opened
7. flew, flue, flough
8. straight, streight, strait
9. tired, tried, tryed
10. pertend, portend, pretend
11. furyous, furious, furrious
12. couldn't, cuoldn't, coudn't
13. laghing, laughing, laffing
14. ensist, innsist, insist
15. principle, principal, prinsipal
16. tommorrow, tomorow, tomorrow
17. cents, sense, sence
18. humor, humer, huemor

Encyclopedia Explorations

This section presents five directed lessons and 19 encyclopedia scavenger hunt sheets. To help your students become comfortable with encyclopedias, use these explorations on a regular basis. When questions arise during class discussions, appoint a student to look up the answer. Encourage students to "check out" an encyclopedia volume during silent reading period.

Before conducting research lessons using encyclopedias, students should have had practice taking notes. (See pages 107–112.)

ACTIVITIES

Info-Mobiles (Page 174)

This hands-on project provides valuable practice in locating and recording information. If your students have not written information from a reference book in their own words, practice this skill before beginning the project.

Animal Books (Page 175)

Students will create informational booklets about animals using encyclopedia articles. Donate these booklets to a younger class for inclusion in that class's library.

Rapid Research (Page 176)

This activity gives students practice in quickly summarizing important information from an encyclopedia article.

Encyclopedia Mural (Page 177)

Small groups of students work together to create a mural depicting items and information found in one volume of a set of encyclopedias.

Travel Time (Page 178)
In this activity, students will create travel posters to show comprehension of information read in an encyclopedia.

Encyclopedia Scavenger Hunt (Pages 179–197)
This section consists of 19 activity sheets that require students to use an encyclopedia to locate information. Each sheet may be completed using one or two volumes of the encyclopedia, minimizing the difficulty of sharing when books are limited.

The tasks range from locating specific facts to presenting information in the form of a chart, map, or drawing. Each page presents at least one task that involves higher-level thinking skills.

Using the Scavenger Hunt Pages

There are several ways to use the Scavenger Hunt pages:

- as individual, partner, or small-group assignments
- students choose a sheet to complete when they have extra time. Students who complete all the sheets during the year may be given a certificate or prize.

Assessment tips:
Due to the open-ended nature of many of the research items on the *Scavenger Hunt* sheets and the large amount of space that would be required to provide answers, we have not included an answer key for this section of the book.

We recommend that you group several students who have completed the same sheet. Ask them to compare answers and then use the following rubric as a guide to evaluate each other's work.

5 All answers are written in complete sentences (except for drawings, charts, and lists). Information is complete and clearly presented. Work is neat.

4 Most answers are written in complete sentences. Information is fairly complete and clearly presented. Work is neat.

3 Several answers are not written in complete sentences. Information is not always clear or complete. Work is fairly neat.

2 Answers are written in fragments. Important information is missing and/or not presented clearly. Work is messy.

1 Many spaces are left blank. Answers are written in fragments. Very little information is given and/or not presented clearly.

Info-Mobiles

Materials (for each student)
- wire coat hanger
- string
- writing paper
- 6 index cards
- hole punch
- one volume of an encyclopedia

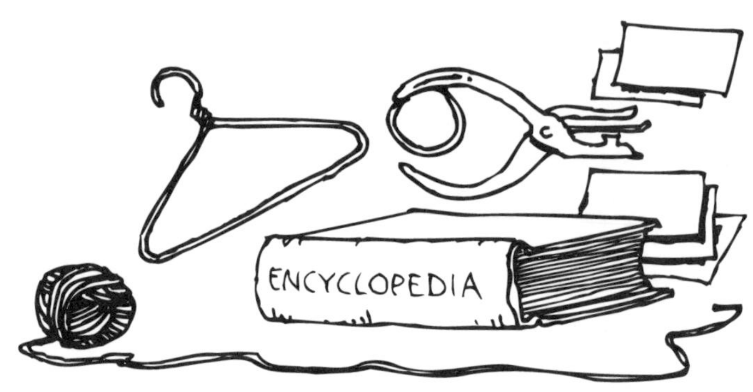

Steps to Follow
1. Each student chooses a topic from the encyclopedia.
2. Write the name of the topic on an index card and punch a hole in the top center of the card. Hang this card in the open space of the coat hanger.
3. Students write (in note form) five important facts about the topic.
4. On each remaining card, convert their notes about one fact to a complete sentence. Punch holes in the cards and suspend them from the coat hanger, using strings of varying lengths.

Animal Books

Brainstorming

Generate a list of questions that the class would like to answer:

What does the animal look like?
Where does it live?
What does it eat?
Who are its enemies and how does it protect itself?

You might wish to use the chart on page 80.

Researching and Writing

1. Write each research question on a small sheet of paper or an index card.
2. Select an animal to research.
3. Read an encyclopedia article about the animal. Make notes as information is found that answers each question. Limit the notes to one or two facts about each question.
4. Write a rough draft, turning the notes into complete sentences. You may wish to use the questions as the "title" for each page.
5. Plan illustrations to go along with your information.

Creating the Booklets

Materials

- white copy paper, cut in half crosswise
- stapler
- colored pencils, crayons, or markers
- 6˝ x 18˝ (15 x 46 cm) construction paper

Steps to Follow

1. Record text and illustrations on the white paper, using the front sides only. Leave a 1˝ (2.5 cm) margin on the left side of the page to allow room for stapling.
2. When all text and illustrations are complete and have been approved, fold the construction paper around the pages to make a cover. Staple near the fold.
3. Decorate the cover of the book. Be sure to include a title and the name of the author and illustrator.

Rapid Research

Materials

- encyclopedias
- transparency of a short encyclopedia article
- chart paper
- note-taking paper or index cards

Group Lesson

1. Read the article on the overhead transparency all the way through together.
2. Examine the article again, one paragraph at a time. Ask students to state the main idea of the paragraph. Write the main idea in note form on the chart.
3. Read each paragraph for supporting details. Write them in note form under the main idea.
4. Point out to students that all the information is written in note form—only the important (key) words have been used.
5. Demonstrate for students how to use the information written on the chart as the basis for an oral presentation.

Individual Student Activity

1. Pass out encyclopedias and paper or index cards to all students.
2. Give a page number that may be found in every volume.
3. Tell students that they have a specific amount of time—perhaps 20 minutes—to study the information in any one article on that page and then make notes on the information. (If the page given is part of a multipage article, assign a new page to those students.)
4. Students make 1-minute presentations of their research to the class or a small group.

Encyclopedia Mural

Materials (for each group)

- sheet of butcher paper
- choice of:
  tempera paints and brushes
  crayons
  markers
- one volume of an encyclopedia

Steps to Follow

1. Divide the class into small groups and give each group an encyclopedia volume.
2. Students are to illustrate some of the information found in their volume. For example, the group with the *S* volume might draw or paint pictures of Saturn, the sun, the process of making soap, snakes, etc.
3. Require students to provide a caption consisting of several facts about each illustration.

Follow-Up

1. Have each group make a presentation of their mural to the entire class.
2. Conduct a discussion about how each group divided the tasks, decided on the information to be reported, and arranged to share the resources.
3. Generate class guidelines for conducting this activity smoothly and cooperatively.
4. Try the experience again using the class guidelines to see if the task is easier.

Travel Time

In preparation for this activity, bring in actual travel posters or large full-color travel ads from magazines. Discuss the type of information presented in the poster or ad. Encourage students to tell what makes each poster or ad effective or ineffective. Create a list of guidelines and suggestions for students to use as they create their own posters.

Materials (for each student or group)

- posterboard or butcher paper
- paints, markers, or crayons
- encyclopedias
- note-taking paper

Steps to Follow

1. Choose a city, state, or country from any volume of the encyclopedia.
2. Read the article and take notes on the most important and interesting features of the place.
3. Choose the type of media (paint, etc.) to use.
4. Create a travel poster featuring attractions and information about that location.

Follow-Up

Students write a brief sales pitch that includes exciting or unusual aspects of their destination. Their goal is to make the other students eager to travel to that location. Students then present their posters to the class, pretending to be a travel agent who wants to "sell" the destination.

Extension

Reproduce the ticket below for each student. After all presentations have been made, students fill out the tickets with the name of the destination they would most like to visit.

Use the tickets to create a graph showing the most popular destinations. Discuss whether the destination itself or the sales pitch had the most impact.

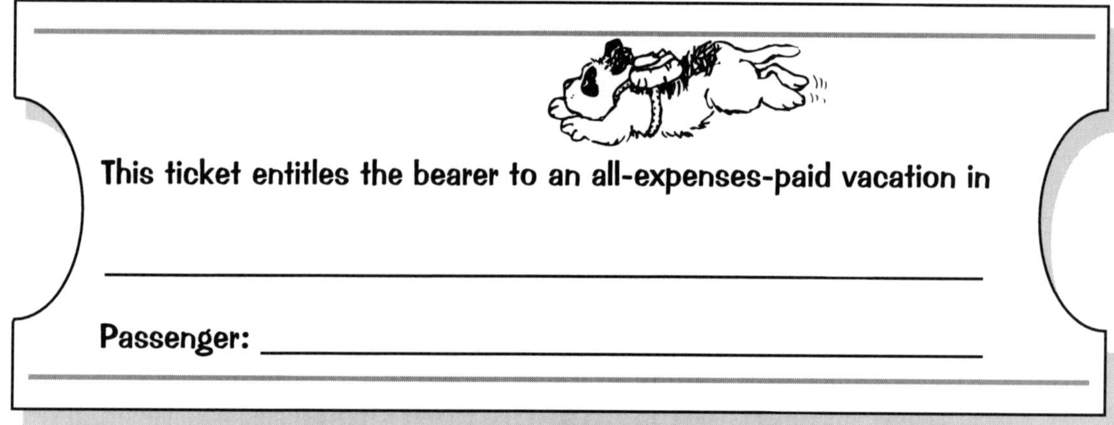

Name:

Encyclopedia Scavenger Hunt A

1. Draw a diagram of an ant's body. Label all important parts.

2. Read an article about any person featured in this volume. Who is the person you chose? Why is this person featured in an encyclopedia? What is the most interesting fact you discovered about this person?

3. Use this outline to complete a portrait of the person you chose.

4. Describe an agouti. Would an agouti make a good pet? Support your answer.

Agouti

5. Draw an outline map of Alabama. Use the map to illustrate one aspect of the state (agricultural products, historical locations, weather, points of interest, etc.).

6. What is azurite and where can it be found?

Name:

Encyclopedia Scavenger Hunt B

1. What are bacteria?

____

Draw and label four different kinds of bacteria.

2. What do Johannes Brahms, Johann Sebastian Bach, and Ludwig van Beethoven have in common?

____

Write a paragraph to explain.

____

____

____

3. Create a graph or chart to show the countries that grow bananas.

4. What kinds of foods do birds eat? List five kinds, and give one example of a bird that eats each type of food.

____

____

____

____

____

5. What is Betelgeuse?

____

What color is it?

____

How large is it?

____

Name:

Encyclopedia Scavenger Hunt C

1. Read about castles. Design a castle of your own and draw a picture of it. Label some of the important parts and give your castle a name.

Welcome to

____

2. Explain why carbon dioxide is:

important: ______________________

useful: ______________________

dangerous: ______________________

3. Make a time line showing important events in the life of Jimmy Carter.

4. Where do cactus plants live?

____

Why are they covered with spines?

____

Choose one kind of cactus to describe in detail.

____

5. What is the color wheel?

____

What are the primary colors?

____

What are the secondary colors?

____

What is your favorite color?

____

Find your favorite color's complementary color.

____

Name:

Encyclopedia Scavenger Hunt D

1. Shade the locations of the major deserts of the world. Label them.

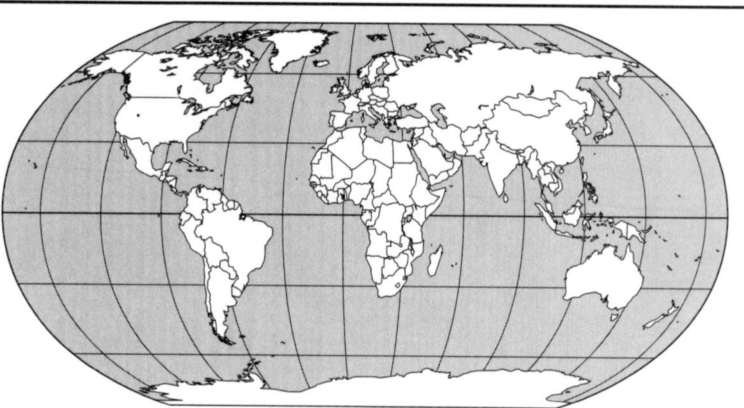

2. Information about several people whose last name is Davis can be found in the encyclopedia. Choose the two that you find most interesting. Write a paragraph comparing and contrasting the lives and accomplishments of the two individuals.

Davis, ______________________ **Davis,** ______________________

____

____

____

3. What breed of dog would you most like to have as a pet? ______________________

Describe, in detail, this dog's appearance. ______________________

____

____

____

4. How do dolphins breathe?

____

____

____

What sense is most valuable to dolphins? Why?

____

____

____

5. Where do most diamonds come from?

____

____

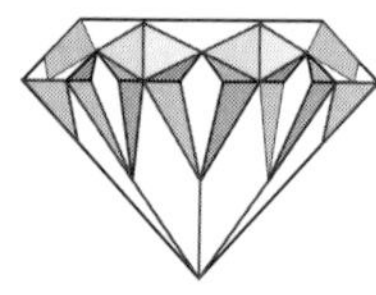

Give three interesting facts about diamonds.

____

____

____

Name:

Encyclopedia Scavenger Hunt E

1. Draw a diagram featuring the layers of the earth. Label each one.

Briefly describe each layer.

____

____

____

____

2. Name the three things Thomas Edison invented.

____

____

____

How do you think his childhood relates to his life's work as an inventor?

____

____

____

____

____

____

3. Describe the food, shelter, and clothing used by traditional Eskimo (Inuit) people.

Food: ______________________________

Shelter: ______________________________

Clothing: ______________________________

4. Draw five faces to illustrate the five basic emotions. Label them.

Tell about a time when you felt one of these emotions.

____

____

5. Where would you go to see edelweiss? What does it look like?

____

____

Name:

Encyclopedia Scavenger Hunt F

1. Fill in the map of France, showing the major rivers, mountain ranges, and cities.

Label the features on the map.

2. Describe the major stages of a frog's life.

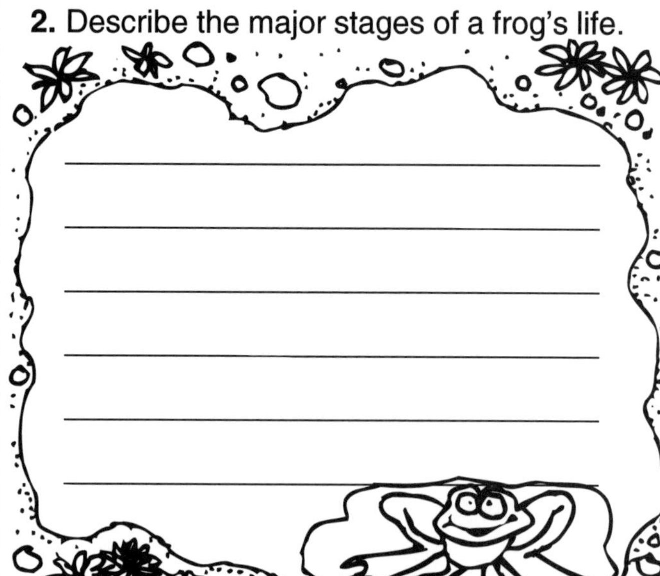

3. If you could live in a forest, which kind of forest would you choose?

Write a poem describing the forest.

4. What is a Fer-de-Lance?

Explain why you would or would not like to own one.

5. Draw a picture to show why Henry Ford is remembered today.

Name:

Encyclopedia Scavenger Hunt G

1. How are geysers formed? Use words and pictures in your explanation.

Welcome To Yellowstone

NATIONAL PARK SERVICE

Department of the Interior

______
______
______
______
______
______

2. What is the difference between a galleon and a galley?

galleon - ______
______
______
______

galley - ______
______
______
______

3. How long did James A. Garfield serve as president? ______

What brought his presidency to an end? ______

______

4. Make a time line showing some of the major gold discoveries in United States history.

5. Where do gorillas live? ______

What do gorillas eat? ______

______

______

What are some problems facing gorillas today? ______

______

______

______

______

Name:

Encyclopedia Scavenger Hunt H

1. Draw a diagram of the human heart. Label it and explain how it works.

2. Describe and illustrate three different kinds of hairstyles from long ago. Be sure to include information about the part of the world where each originated.

3. Briefly explain the history of Halloween.

4. Read about Sir Edmund Hillary and Thor Heyerdahl. What do the two have in common?

   Which one's accomplishments seem more important to you?

   Why?

5. Make a list of the products grown or produced in Hawaii.

Name:

Encyclopedia Scavenger Hunt I

1. Draw a picture of an invention that you think has helped mankind. Write a short paragraph about the invention, telling who invented it and when, and why you think the invention was important.

2. How do icebergs form?

3. Would you prefer to live in Idaho, Iowa, Illinois, or Indiana? ______

Idaho
Iowa
Illinois
Indiana

Why? ______

What features of the state appeal to you?

______

In which of these states would you least like to live? ______

Why? ______

4. Find two facts about insects that you did not already know.

1. ______

2. ______

5. What are considered to be Washington Irving's greatest works?

______ By Washington Irving

______ By Washington Irving

Name:

Encyclopedia Scavenger Hunt JK

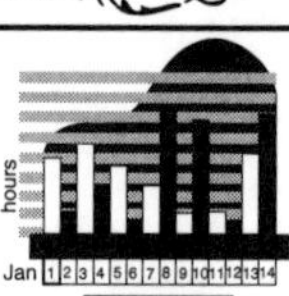

1. Create a chart or table to show important events that have taken place in January.

2. Why is Helen Keller an inspiration to many people?

3. What does a kinkajou do during the day?

What does a Komodo dragon do during the day?

4. List several products made from the fruit of the kapok tree.

5. Find information about three different people whose last name is Jackson.

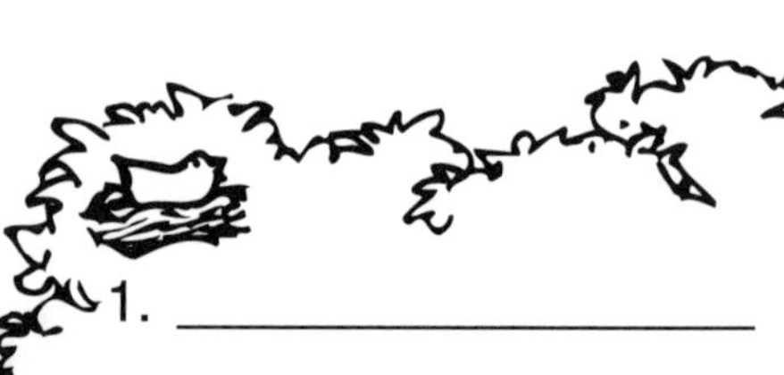

Jackson Family Tree

1.

2.

3.

Name:

Encyclopedia Scavenger Hunt L

1. What is a labyrinth?

____

____

Draw a picture of one to illustrate your answer.

2. What kind of animal is a locust?

____

What kinds of problems can be caused by locusts?

____

____

____

3. Describe some activities and points of interest that might be enjoyed on a visit to Los Angeles.

____

____

____

____

____

4. Create a chart or table giving information about some of the world's largest lakes.

5. Why is Juliette Gordon Low remembered today?

____

____

____

Name:

Encyclopedia Scavenger Hunt M

1. Draw and label the phases of the moon.

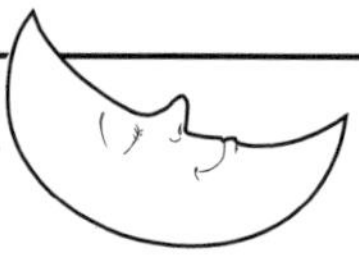

2. What is metal?

Make a list of several kinds of metals and their uses.

Metal	Use

3. Complete the map of the state of Maine, showing some of the products produced there.

4. How is a macaque similar to a mandrill?

How is it different?

5. Who was Rocky Marciano?

Name:

Encyclopedia Scavenger Hunt NO

1. Create a drawing or diagram that shows the body parts of an oyster. Label the parts.

2. Compare the climates of North Carolina and North Dakota. Write a paragraph or use charts and tables to show the differences in temperature and rainfall.

3. Which National Park is nearest to your home?

   ____

   Which National Parks have you visited?

   ____

   ____

   ____

   Which would you most like to visit?

   ____

4. Make a list of plants that are members of the nightshade family.

   ____

   ____

   ____

   Why did many people once believe that tomatoes were poisonous?

   ____

   ____

   ____

5. Write a poem about the opossum. Make sure to include some factual information in your poem.

   ____

   ____

   ____

   ____

   ____

Name:

Encyclopedia Scavenger Hunt P

1. What is Paricutin? ____________________
Draw a series of pictures showing how it was formed.

2. Explain the differences between the petrel and the ptarmigan.

____
____
____
____

3. How is penicillin made and what is it used for?

____
____
____
____

4. Make a chart or drawing that shows how plants are helpful to humans.

5. Who were the two United States presidents whose last names began with *P*? Write three facts about each one.

President ____________________
____
____
____

President ____________________
____
____
____

Name:

Encyclopedia Scavenger Hunt QR

1. Create a time line showing several important events of our country's Revolutionary War. Be prepared to explain why these events were important.

2. What is the Rosetta Stone?

____

____

Where was it found and why is it important?

____

____

____

____

3. Which parts of the world have the most rainfall?

____

____

____

Why?

____

____

____

4. How does a mother rabbit care for her newborn young?

____

____

____

____

____

____

5. What would you do with a quince?

____

____

____

What would you do with a quoit?

____

____

____

Name:

Encyclopedia Scavenger Hunt 8

1. Draw a picture illustrating an important safety rule. Write a sentence under your picture explaining the rule.

2. What do Philip Sheridan and William T. Sherman have in common?

What are some differences between the two men?

3. Make a diagram showing the structure of the skin. Label all parts.

4. Make a list of products that are made from the soybean.

5. Which would make a better dinner, a sole or a sturgeon?

Explain your answer.

Name:

Encyclopedia Scavenger Hunt T

1. Draw a picture illustrating the parts of a tree. Label all parts.

2. Is a tarantula dangerous?

Explain your answer.

3. Read about Tennessee and Texas. Make a list of interesting sights that could be seen on a visit to one of these states.

Tennessee

Texas

4. Make a diagram showing the parts of a tooth. Label all parts.

5. Briefly tell the story of the *Titanic.*

Name:

Encyclopedia Scavenger Hunt UV

1. Make a chart showing several plant parts used as vegetables.

2. Who were the Vikings?

Write a paragraph about the Vikings and how they lived.

3. Many countries have a tomb for unknown soldiers. Where in the United States is this monument located?

4. What are some Valentine's Day customs of the past?

5. Describe the three branches of the United States government.

Name:

Encyclopedia Scavenger Hunt WXYZ

1. Draw a diagram of a whale's body. Label all parts.

2. Why do tourists visit Williamsburg?

What can they see and do there?

3. What is the difference between xenon and Xenophon?

4. List five facts about zinc.

5. Using words and pictures, present as much information as possible about the yak.

Reading Reference Materials
Chapter 3

Atlas Adventures

This section contains a variety of activities involving the use of an atlas. It is not intended to teach specific map skills, but rather to allow students to become comfortable and fluent with an atlas. Be sure that your students have the requisite map skills before beginning any of the activities.

Not all information may be obtainable in every atlas. It is desirable to have several different atlases from which to choose.

ACTIVITIES

Geography: An Introductory Game (Page 200)

This fast-paced game encourages students to scan the atlas, looking for places that begin with specific letters.

What's in an Atlas? (Page 201)

This activity, which may be done by individuals or small groups, will familiarize students with the differences in content of the atlases available to them. Gather as many different atlases as you can for this lesson.

After students have completed page 201, allow time for them to present the information they found. Compile a class chart listing unique features of each atlas so that students know which atlas to refer to for specific types of maps and information.

Types of Maps in an Atlas (Pages 202 and 203)

This activity provides practice in identifying types of maps most often used. Students read the description of each type of map given on page 202. They then locate and label it on page 203.

Create a Country (Pages 204–208)

Students create an imaginary country, including three types of maps.

Cruising the Atlas (Page 209)

Assign each student or group of students a particular body of water to research. Use any ocean, sea, or lake. Using the various maps in an atlas, students complete their record sheets.

Capital Cities of the World (Page 210)

Decorate a bulletin board with stars containing information about capital cities around the world.

Geography: An Introductory Game

Materials

- one world atlas for every 1 to 2 students (atlases may be different editions)

How to Play

1. Write the name of any continent, country, state, or city on the board.
2. Students use their atlases to find another location name that begins with the last letter of the word written on the board. For example, if you give *Amsterdam,* students must find a place name beginning with the letter *M.*
3. Call on a student to come to the board and record the new place name.
4. Play continues in this manner until the class is stumped or interest wanes.

Variations

- For a faster version, play orally, without writing the place names on the board. This may be done in small groups as well.
- Start the class off with a place name and allow them to make their own individual written lists, following the same rule. Play for a given time period and see who has recorded the most place names. (Each name may be used only once on a list.)

Name:

What's in an Atlas?

Name of atlas, including publisher: ______________________

Use your atlas to answer the questions and find the information requested on this sheet.

1. Does your atlas have a **table of contents**? ______________________

If so, how is it arranged? (Give several examples.) ______________________

____

2. In what part of the atlas is the **index** located? ______________________

On what page does the index begin? ______________________

3. What information is given about each index entry? ______________________

4. Does your atlas contain photographs? ______________________

5. Does your atlas have any graphs? ______________________

Does your atlas have:	Yes	No	Comments
Separate physical and political maps			
Combined physical and political maps			
Climate maps			
Rainfall maps			
Population maps			
Vegetation maps			
Natural resource maps			
Maps that show things produced			
Road maps			
Maps that show wildlife			
A separate map of each continent			
Information in paragraph form			

6. Do you think this atlas is easy to read and use?

Why or why not? ______________________

____

Name:

Types of Maps in an Atlas

There are many types of maps. Here are some of the most common maps you find in atlases.

Political Maps...
- show boundaries between countries, states, counties
- show capitals and other cities
- show the basic shape and size of the countries, states, counties

Physical Maps...
- show what the land looks like
- show terrain features such as:
  mountain ranges
  plains
  rivers and lakes
  elevations

Population Maps...
- show the number of people in an area
- use symbols to represent people

Crop or Produce Maps...
- show crops grown
- show animals raised
- show products manufactured

Weather Maps...
- show major weather situations
- use symbols to represent weather

Time Zone Maps...
- show the time in various parts of a country, continent, or the world

Check in your atlas and mark off the maps you were able to find:

- ☐ Political
- ☐ Physical
- ☐ Population
- ☐ Crop or Produce
- ☐ Weather
- ☐ Time Zone

Name:

Find the Maps

Use an atlas to find these different types of maps.

Political	**Physical**	**Population**
Crop or Produce	**Weather**	**Time Zone**

Type of map found:	This map shows:	Page in atlas:

Name of atlas used: ______________________________

Create a Country

Students will create an imaginary country, including three types of maps.

- physical
- political
- product/resource

pages 205–208

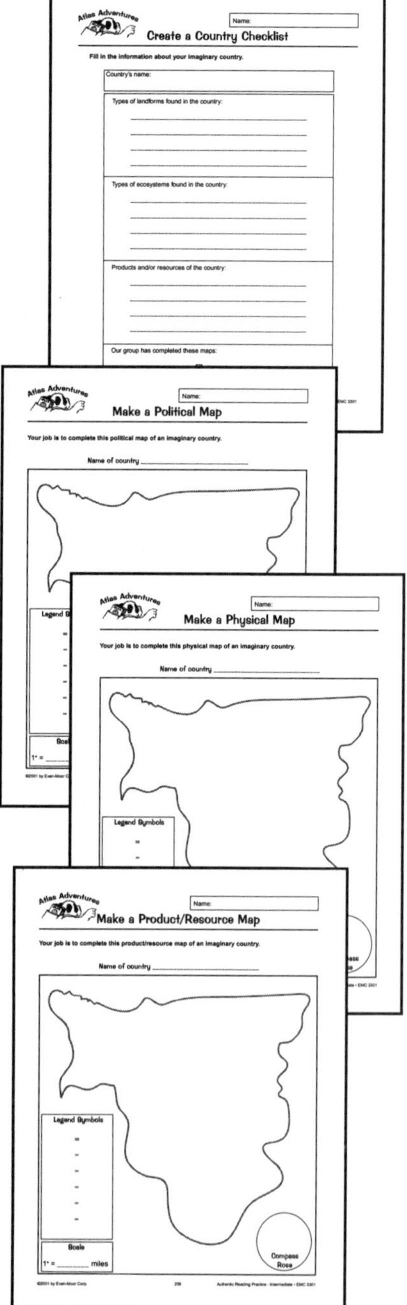

Preparation

1. You will need atlases that contain examples of the types of maps listed above.
2. Spend time as a class examining these three types of maps and listing the features of each on charts. These charts will serve as guides as students “create a country.”
3. Reproduce pages 205–208 for each group to use as they create a country.

Steps to Follow

1. Divide students into small groups with the assignment of creating an imaginary country. Provide each group with several atlases and a sheet of butcher paper or posterboard.
2. Students brainstorm within their group to decide on the characteristics of their country (landscape forms, weather conditions, types of products and resources). Record notes on the checklist form.
3. Each map must be given a name!

Name:

Create a Country Checklist

Fill in the information about your imaginary country.

Country's name:

Types of landforms found in the country:

____

____

____

____

Types of ecosystems found in the country:

____

____

____

____

Products and/or resources of the country:

____

____

____

____

Our group has completed these maps:

- ☐ physical
- ☐ political
- ☐ product/resources

Name:

Make a Political Map

Your job is to complete this political map of an imaginary country.

Name of country ______________________________

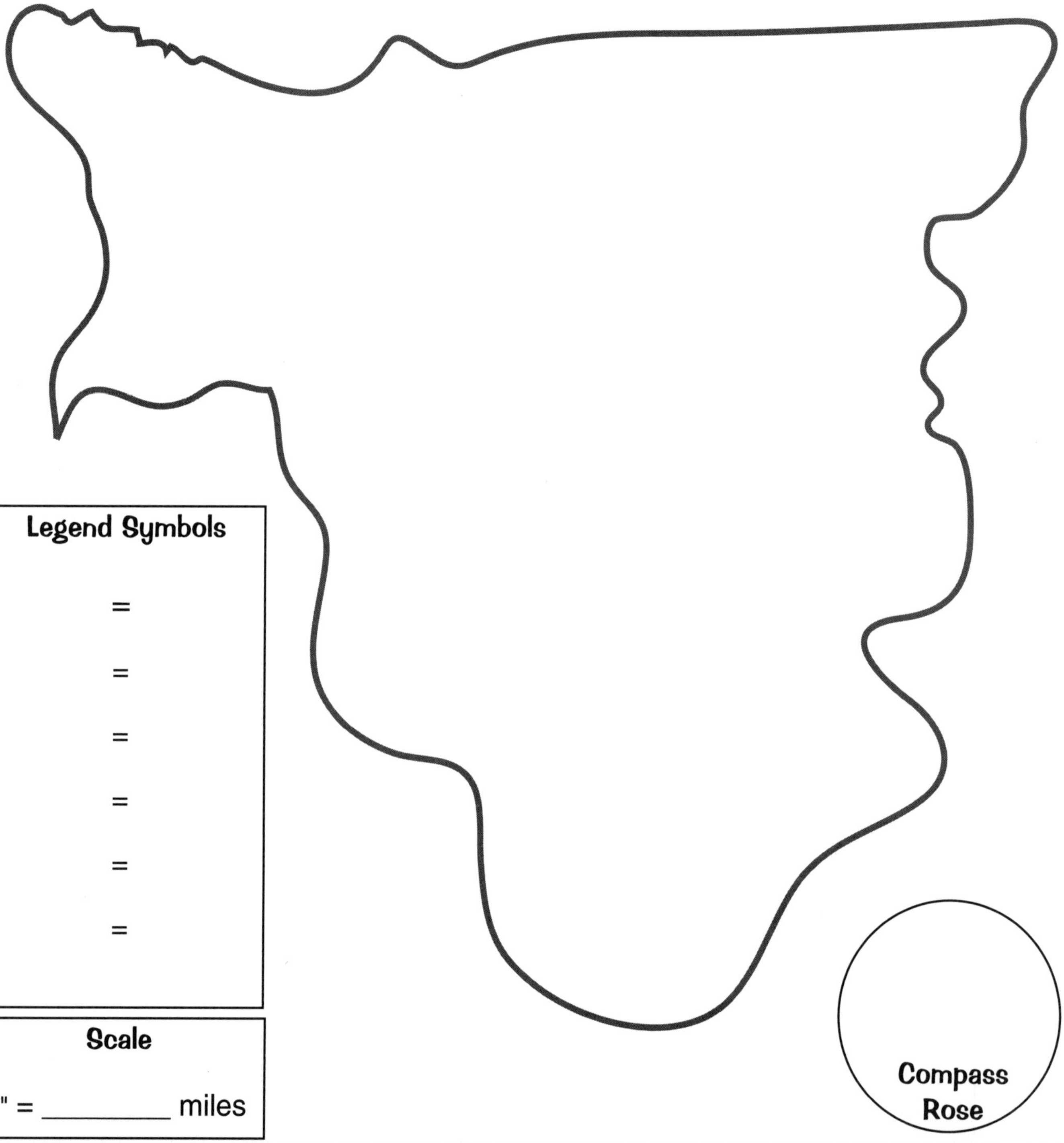

Legend Symbols

=

=

=

=

=

=

Scale

1" = _________ miles

Compass Rose

Name:

Make a Physical Map

Your job is to complete this physical map of an imaginary country.

Name of country ______________________________

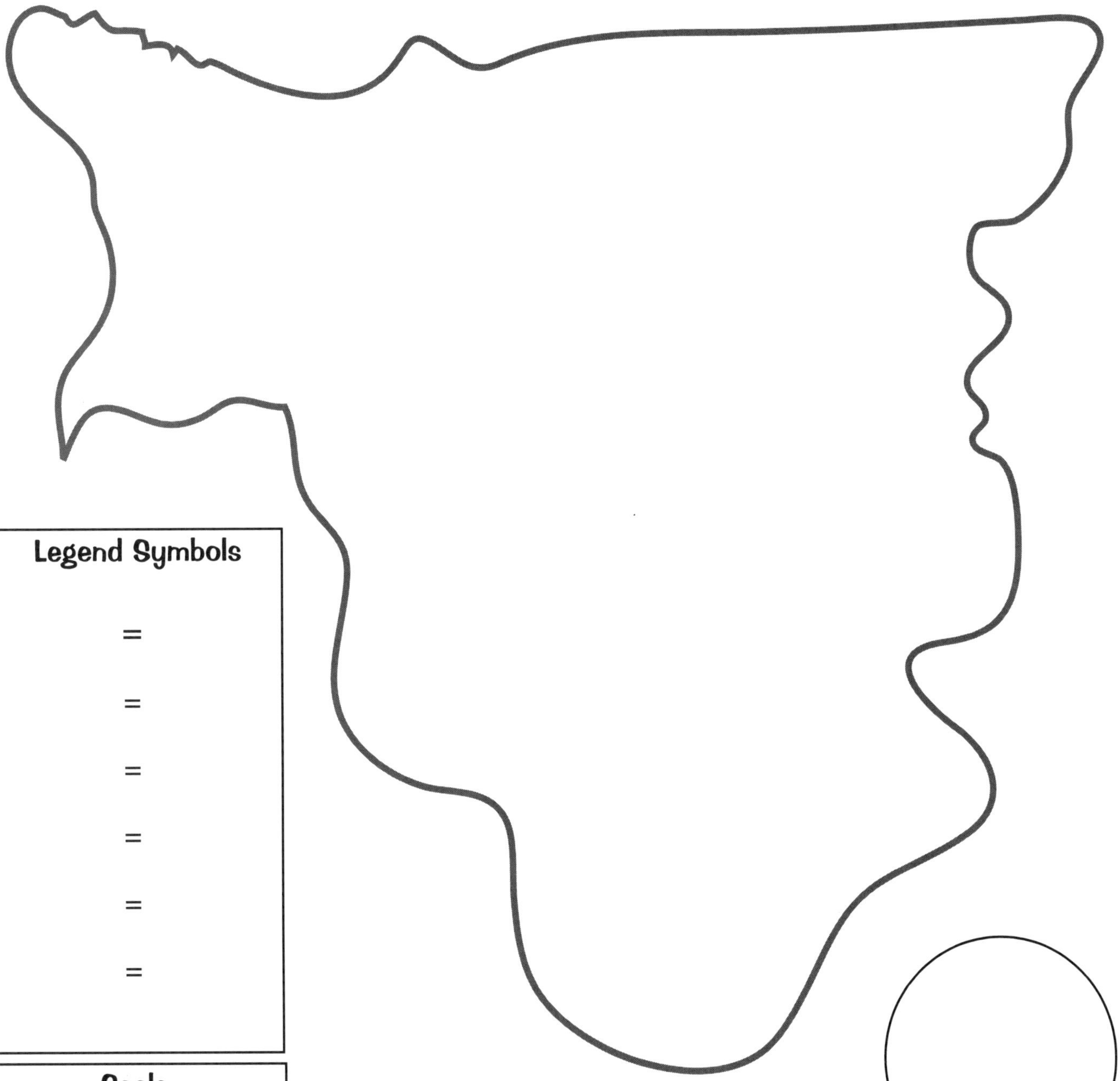

Legend Symbols

=

=

=

=

=

=

Scale

1" = ________ miles

Compass Rose

Atlas Adventures

Name:

Make a Product/Resource Map

Your job is to complete this product/resource map of an imaginary country.

Name of country ____________________

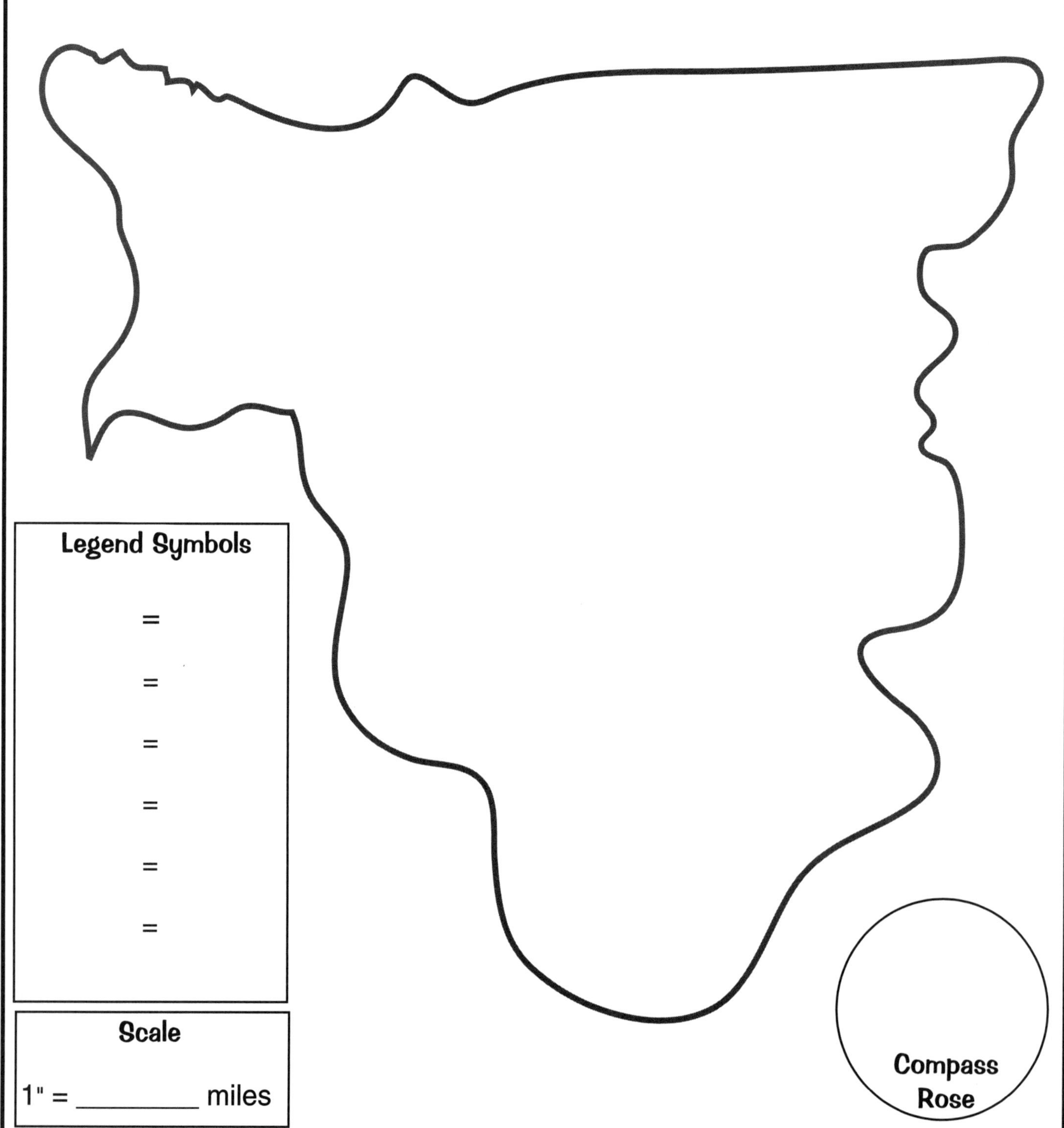

Name:

Cruising the Atlas

Name of atlas,
including publisher: ____________________

Find a body of water: ____________________

On or near what continent is it located? ____________________

What countries or states touch this body of water? ____________________

____

Name any large cities located on or near this body of water. ____________________

____

What type of climate is found in the area of this body of water? ____________________

____

Use the scale of miles on the map to measure the size of this body of water.

____

Describe the route you would take if you were to visit this body of water. Use directional words. ____________________

____

____

On the world map below, show the location of your body of water with a red X.

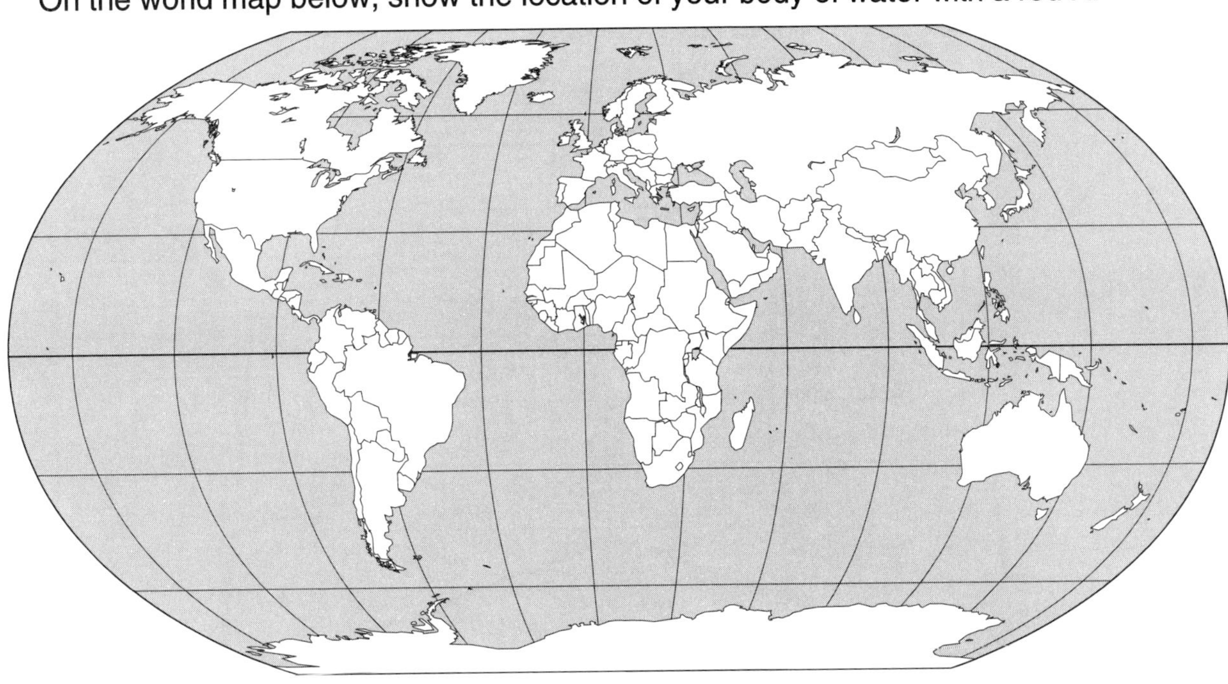

Capital Cities of the World

Preparation

1. Provide an atlas for each student if possible. They need not be the same edition.
2. Brainstorm with the class to come up with a list of the countries of the world. There should be twice as many countries as students in the class.
3. Each student chooses two countries. (Or they might draw countries from a hat.)
4. Reproduce two stars for each student.

Student Activity

Students write on the stars the following information about their countries' capitals:

- the name of the city and country
- population of the city
- geographical location (in the Andes Mountains, on the Atlantic Ocean, etc.)
- physical, historical, or cultural features (encyclopedias may be needed)

Display all the stars on a bulletin board or string them together and hang along the classroom wall. Try to collect enough to reach all the way around the classroom!

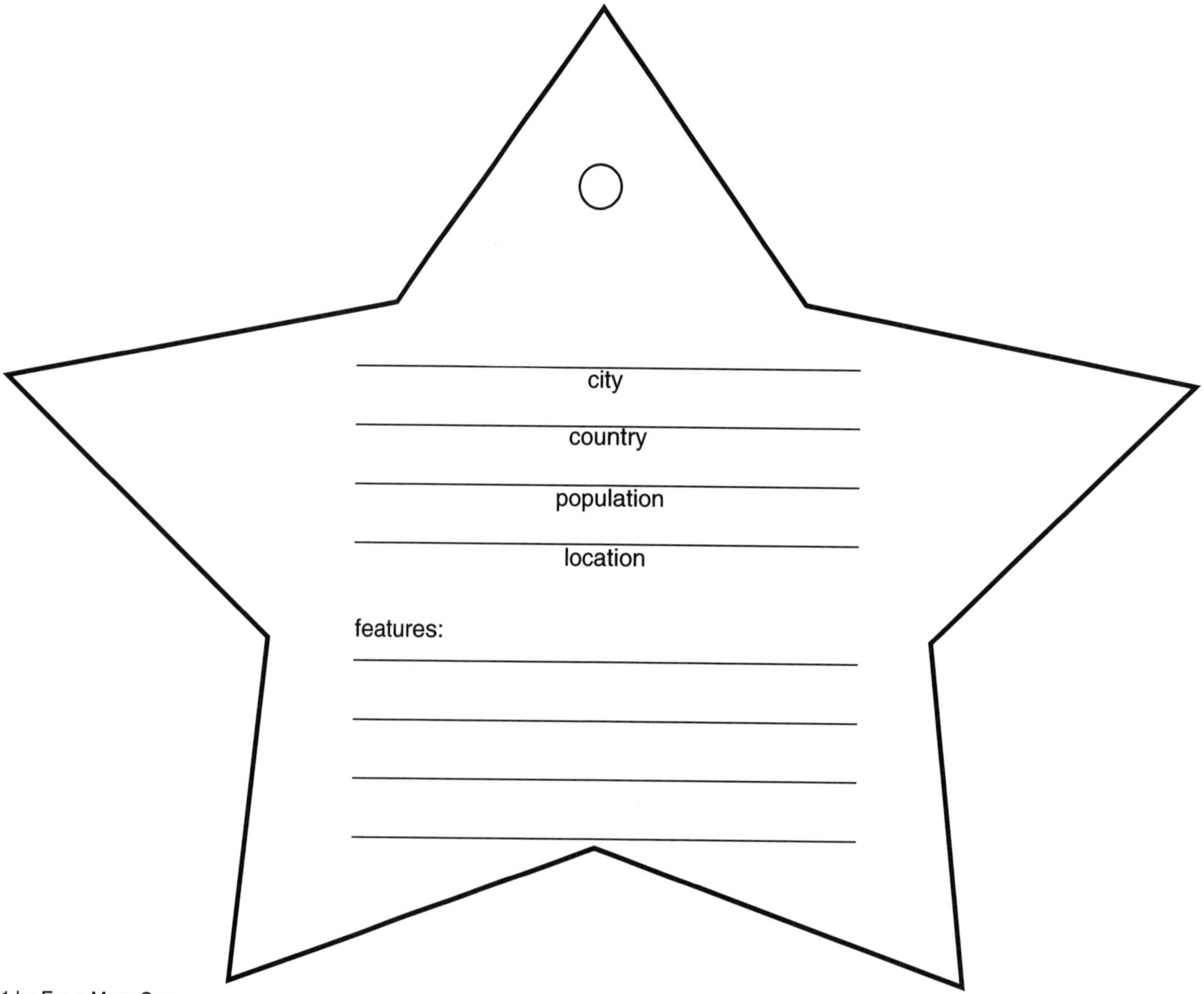

____
city

____
country

____
population

____
location

features:

____

____

____

____

Reading Reference Materials Skills Checklist 

	Students' Names								
Dictionary Skills									
Locates words									
Understands word meaning									
Chooses correct meaning for context									
Categorizes words									
Uses dictionary for correct spellings									
Encyclopedia Skills									
Locates information in an encyclopedia									
Reports information in a variety of forms									
Shows understanding of articles read									
Atlas Skills									
Understands what an atlas contains									
Identifies different types of maps									
Finds locations in an atlas									
Uses an atlas index									

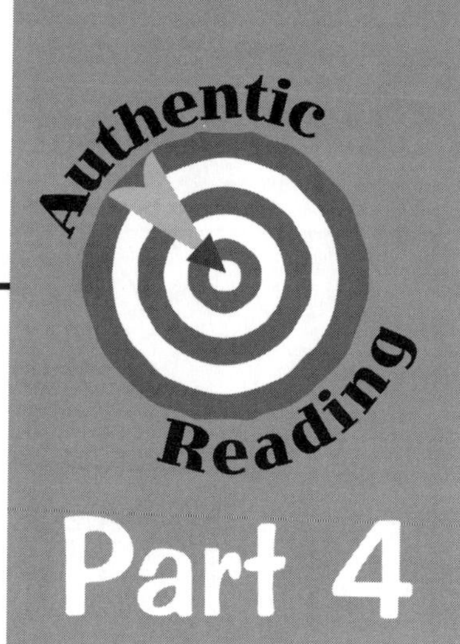

Reading Newspapers & Magazines

Newspapers and magazines are a logical choice for authentic reading in the classroom. Students increase their reading skills while becoming more informed on a variety of topics. Motivation is high, as students have many choices of attractive and pertinent material to read.

ACTIVITIES

Getting and Using Newspapers (Page 214)

Activities to Introduce the Newspaper (Pages 215–219)

The four activities in this section will help students become familiar with what is in the newspaper and newspaper formats.

Parts of the Newspaper (Pages 220–227)

Familiarize students with the standard parts of a newspaper, from sports and weather to classified ads.

Note: Pages 225 and 226 contain activities about political cartoons. Because understanding the message of political cartoons requires some knowledge of current events and personalities, you may want to build a collection of cartoons that contain a more obvious message. Reproduce some on transparencies and use them to introduce the concept.

Creative Newspaper Activities (Pages 228–234)

Use the newspaper to learn new words, create a journal, or champion a cause.

Note: Page 229 provides practice in locating the names of famous people in the newspaper. After students have completed this worksheet, you may wish to compile a "People in the News" class notebook. Create a page for each famous person. Write the name, the date, and a sentence telling why the person was in the news. Each time you see that person in the newspaper, add to his or her page in the same manner.

Create a Class Newspaper (Pages 235–240)

Planning and execution tips simplify the process of producing a class newspaper.

Getting and Using Newspapers

How to Get Newspapers for Your Classroom

- Find out about a national program called **Newspapers in Education (NIE),** which encourages the use of newspapers in classrooms. Many local newspapers have NIE coordinators who work directly with teachers, often pairing them with sponsors whose donations pay for a weekly class set of newspapers for the entire school year. Contact your local newspaper for details.

- Ask students to bring in yesterday's paper from home each day. You might assign several different students to each day of the week as part of their regular homework assignments.

- Request PTA or instructional materials funds to purchase several newspaper subscriptions for your classroom. Newspapers will often discount their subscription rates to schools.

Make It a Daily Event

- Choose several articles from the paper. Divide the class into small groups and assign each group an article to read and discuss. Ask each group to appoint a spokesperson to briefly present the information from the article to the class.

- Use the time immediately following lunch as newspaper time. Play some recorded music as the students return from lunch. Allow them to choose a section of newspaper to read for 15 or 20 minutes. This makes for a very nice period of sustained silent reading. Extend the time to up to 30 minutes for classes that show interest. Take time to discuss what students have read.

- Direct students to read any article of their choosing and write a brief summary in a notebook kept for this purpose. Remind them to date the summary. The next day, the student will look for a related article to read and summarize. This exercise may be continued throughout the year and will help students to observe relationships and connections between subjects.

Name:

Newspaper Scavenger Hunt

Get more familiar with what is in a newspaper. Find each of the features or items listed below. Cut out the articles or items and attach them to a large piece of paper entitled "Find It in the Newspaper." Cut out the labels below and attach them next to the correct feature.

A Weather Report	**A Favorite Food**
A TV Guide	**A Favorite Sport**
A Comic Strip with 4 Sections	**A Favorite Comic Strip**
A Recipe	**A Favorite Car**
A Classified Ad for a Computer	**A Favorite TV Program**
A Puzzle	**A Favorite Movie**
A Letter to the Editor	**A Word That Describes You**
A Sports Picture	**A Favorite Pet**
A Grocery Store Ad	**A Number to Match Your Age**
An Obituary	**A Job You Would Like to Have**
A Help Wanted Ad	**Something You Would Like to Buy**
A Movie Guide	**A News Story That Interests You**

Name:

Getting Acquainted with Your Newspaper

DOG WORLD

Newspapers are divided into sections. Each section focuses on a different type of information. A typical newspaper might have these sections:

- **National and International News**
- **Local News**
- **Classified Ads**
- **Stock Market Reports**
- **Sports**
- **Entertainment**

How many different sections are in your newspaper? ________

An **index** to the newspaper can usually be found on the front page of the paper. Use your index to write the section and page number where these features can be found.

Weather __________ Sports ____________

Comics ___________ Car Ads ___________

Editorials _________ Television _________

News in a paper can be divided into four different types:

- **International News**
  News about other countries
- **National News**
  News about the United States
- **State News**
  News about your state
- **Local News**
  News about your community

Find an example of each kind of news in your newspaper.
Write the title of the article.

1. International: ______________________________

2. National: ______________________________

3. State: ______________________________

4. Local: ______________________________

The "5 W's" Game

Reading newspapers is facilitated if students know that all good news stories answer the "5 W's"—Who, What, Where, When, and Why.

Materials
- a simple news story reproduced on an overhead transparency
- simple stories cut out from the newspaper for individual students
- page 218, reproduced for each student
- for the activity center—five containers, each labeled with one of the 5 W's

Steps to Follow
1. Write the 5 W's on the chalkboard and explain them to the class.
2. As a group, read the news story on the transparency and practice finding the 5 W's.
3. Give each student or pair of students a news story and a copy of page 218.
4. Discuss the directions together to be sure students understand that the 5 W's phrases should form a sentence when read in order.
5. When the worksheets are complete, have students cut apart the 5 W's phrases and place each strip in the appropriate container.

Follow-Up
As an independent center activity, students draw a slip from each of the five containers and then read them in order to form the lead sentence of a zany news story. For an extra challenge, students may write a news story based on that lead sentence.

Who the president of the local bank

What jumped into a vat of chocolate

Where at the Little League park

When at 3:00 a.m.

Why to get warm

Name:

The "5 W's" Game 2

Newspaper reporters must be sure to cover all the facts when they write about events that happen. They use the 5 W's to help them. The 5 W's are Who, What, Where, When, and Why.

Read a short newspaper article to find out **who** the story is about, **what** happened, **when** it happened, **where** it happened, and **why** it happened. Fill in each blank space below with a simple phrase so that a complete sentence is formed when the phrases are read in order.

For example, a ***Who, What, Where, When***, and ***Why Game*** report on a UFO sighting might read like this:

Who A large, shiny UFO

What was seen flying

Where over Lake Michigan

When last night

Why to locate sunken spacecraft

Your teacher will give you instructions for what to do with your 5 W's phrases. Be ready for some zany fun!

Who ______________________

What ______________________

Where ______________________

When ______________________

Why ______________________

"5 W's" Posters

This exploration works well in small group, partner, or individual formats.

Materials

- posterboard
- a newspaper article
- scissors
- glue
- markers

Steps to Follow

1. Direct students to choose an article to read and discuss. Students should isolate from the article the 5 W's of journalism:

   Who the story was about
   What happened
   Where it happened
   When it happened
   Why it happened

   Each of these W's should be answered with simple phrases or sentences and arranged on the poster in a manner that is easy to read.

2. Pictures, drawings, and words or letters cut from headlines can enhance the poster. The design of the poster should be clear and attractive.

3. Remind students that the purpose of a poster is to impart information quickly and often from some distance away. Long chunks of text and small lettering will be ineffective. The goal is to transmit the essence of the story in a succinct way.

NASA
SHOWS NEW SPACECRAFT
J.P.L. Pasadena
Tuesday, July 2, 2001
Replaces Space Shuttles.

Salmon Derby
Friday ~ Sunday
$10.00 Entrance fee
Raise money for salmon and trout project.

REELECTED
MAYOR
Harry Smith
Ourtown U.S.A.
July 2001
Beat Challenger Ben Jones

Name:

Front Page News

Look at the front pages of two different newspapers with the same date.

- Write the name of each paper at the top of one of the columns below.
- In each column, write the front page headlines in the order of importance with which they were treated by that paper. Largest headlines and those at the top of the page are more important.

Name of Newspaper	Name of Newspaper

Sports Page

This popular section is the perfect tool to entice unenthusiastic readers to dig into the daily paper. There are numerous ways to use this section.

1. Students can keep scrapbooks of their favorite sports teams and/or players. If several students in the class share an interest in a particular team or sport, they can form a fan club and work together to create a scrapbook. Make time available occasionally for fan clubs to present updates on their teams, using the material in their scrapbooks.

2. The sports section is full of numbers! Students are using important reading skills such as scanning to locate numbers and skimming for key words to let them know they have located the correct number.

   Create math problems based on the information found in the sports pages. Here are some examples. When you examine a sports section for yourself, you will undoubtedly come up with lots more ideas.

   - Find the total points scored by professional basketball (or football or baseball) teams in games played yesterday.
   - What is the total number of wins among teams in a given conference or league? Total number of losses?
   - How many games (total) have been played so far this season?
   - How many games separate the team that has won the most times from the team that has won the fewest times?
   - Which team scored the most points in a single game yesterday?

3. Ask each student to read an article about a sports personality and write a short summary of the article on a 5" x 7" index card (another opportunity to practice the 5 W's). Collect the cards to create a class file on sports players. You might label one file "Good Sports" for positive articles and one file "Bad Sports" for negative articles.

Weather Information

Use the weather page to practice reading geographical names as well as reading information in the form of charts or tables and then translating this information into graphs.

1. Create a class chart showing the local weather over an extended period of time. Record high and low daily temperatures, precipitation, and a pictorial description of the day's weather (sunny, cloudy, rainy, etc.).

Weather Watch
APRIL

MON	TUE	WED	THUR	FRI
	1 HI 68 LO 56	2 HI 64 LO 52	3 HI 66 LO 54	4 HI 72 LO 56
7 HI 70 LO 56	8 HI 67 LO 54	9 HI 66 LO 58	10 HI 65 LO 58	11 HI 64 LO 56
14 HI 64 LO 50	15 HI 63 LO 52	16 HI 64 LO 51	17	18
21	22	23	24	25
28	29	30		

Our Weather

sunny partly sunny cloudy

rain thunderstorms snow

2. Track the high temperature forecast for the next day. Plot it on a line graph using a red marker. Plot the actual high temperature for that day using a blue marker. Connect the points with lines of the same colors. Discuss the information that can be "read" on the graph after a week or so of entries.

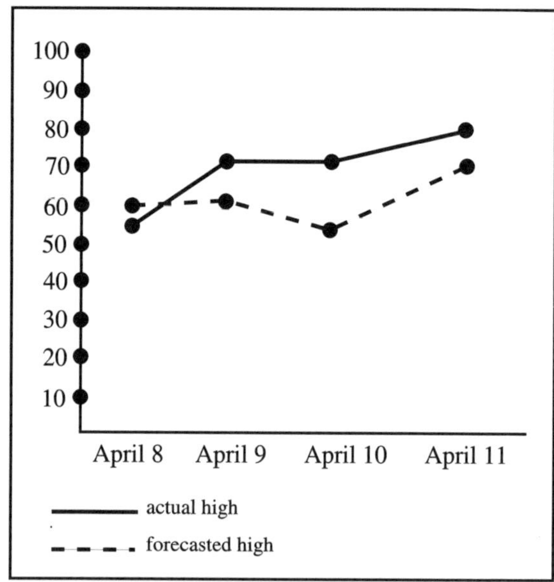

3. Challenge students to use the cities and countries named on the weather page to write Geographic Riddles. In the process they may need to look up information in an almanac, atlas, or other reference materials. Post the riddles in a center with maps, globes, and reference books. (This is a homework activity that the whole family can have fun with.)

He may have sailed the ocean blue in 1492, but this city isn't even on the sea.

(Columbus, Ohio)

I sound like I might be roaming the great plains, but I'm really found in New York.

(Buffalo, New York)

No, I am not related to that giant ape!

(Hong Kong)

Human Interest Stories

Human interest stories are not news in the true sense of the word, but they are often some of the most engaging, and occasionally uplifting, stories to be found in the newspaper.

- Bring in two or three human interest stories that you think might be of interest to your students. Over the course of a week or so, read the stories to the class. Discuss the stories. Ask questions such as:

  Why were these stories printed in the newspaper?

  What do they have in common?
  Do you consider these stories to be news? Why or why not?

  Define some characteristics of a good human interest story.

- Tell the students that they are going to become reporters. Ask them to find a human interest story—one that really happened to a friend or family member.

- Have students write their stories, being sure to include interviews and illustrations. Photographs to accompany the stories are ideal, but students without access to cameras can "draw" their photographs.

- Require students to meet with peer committees to review and edit their work. Finally, ask students to create final copies of their stories for "publishing." Compile the stories into a class book.

  Some students might wish to submit their stories to school or local newspapers for consideration.

Letters to the Editor

Save a number of consecutive issues of a newspaper. Locate an article that generated several letters to the editor. Copy the article and the letters for use in class.

- Read the article with your students. Discuss the students' reactions to what they have read.

- Next, share the letters to the editor with your students. Evaluate the letters. Ask questions such as:

  Do you think the writer of this letter understands the article?

  Does the writer do a good job of explaining his/her position or reaction?

  Are his/her points based more on rational thought or emotion?

  Which of the letters is most effective?

- Direct students to locate a newspaper article that inspires them to respond. (This can be a great homework assignment!) Instruct students to read the article and bring it to class. Remind them to be sure to bring along the address to which letters to the editor should be sent.

- Have students outline a response to the editor and then write it in letter form. Work in partners or teams to make sure that spelling and grammar are correct and that the letters are in the proper form.

  Send the letters to the editors of the newspaper. Follow up to see if they are printed.

Name:

Political Cartoons

On the editorial page of most newspapers, you will find a **political cartoon**. The cartoonist presents his/her opinion of an event, elected official, or situation in a humorous and often exaggerated way.

- Find a political cartoon that you think is interesting (you can agree or disagree with the message).
- Cut it out and glue it on this page.
- Below the cartoon, write a paragraph explaining its meaning.

Paste cartoon here.

Name:

Political Cartoons 2

You have picked a political cartoon and written an explanation of its message. Now create a cartoon that gives the opposite message. Below the cartoon, write a paragraph explaining why you agree or disagree with the message of the cartoon you created.

Classified Ads

The classified ads of your local newspaper are a bountiful source of information. Through classified ads one can find employment opportunities, buy and sell items ranging from motorcycles to real estate, or seek lost items. Knowing how to use the classified ad section of the paper is a valuable skill for your students.

Collect enough classified ad sections so that each student has one to work with. These do not need to come from the same newspaper or share the same date. Use the classified ads for the following activities:

- What is the average rental price of a two-bedroom apartment in your area? Use ads for at least three apartments to determine your average.
- In what fields are jobs being offered? List four different job opportunities.
- Read the ads for used automobiles. Which car would you most like to buy? Write a description of the car and give its price.
- Locate the lost and found column. Usually you will see ads for lost dogs and cats. Are there ads for any other lost items? What are they?

- How much does it cost to place an ad in this newspaper? If the price is not printed in the pages of the ad section, encourage students to call the newspaper to inquire about the price of a weekly ad. If you are using a variety of papers, compare the costs of the ads.
- Ask friends and relatives from other sections of the country to send the classified section from their local newspaper. Ask students to draw conclusions about an area based on reading the classified ads. (If there are lots of ads for horses and tractors, you are probably reading the ads from a rural area. If there are lots of ads for surfboards, you're probably near the beach, etc.)

Name:

Learning New Words

Reading the newspaper each day is a good way to improve your vocabulary. Although you may not be familiar with some of the words you see in the headlines, you can often get the meaning from the surrounding words.

Look at the circled words in these headlines. Write what you think the word means. Then check a dictionary to see if you are right. Rewrite the headline in your own words.

Environmentalists call for protection of imperiled marine mammals

- I think "imperiled" means ____________________
- My headline: ____________________

Incumbent, challengers vie for city council seat

- I think "incumbent" means ____________________
- My headline: ____________________

Revelers warned to contain fireworks

- I think "revelers" means ____________________
- My headline: ____________________

Chinese dissident freed after 6 years

- I think "dissident" means ____________________
- My headline ____________________

EXTRA! EXTRA!

Find four words in the newspaper that are unfamiliar to you. Write them on a piece of paper. Guess what they mean using the context of the sentence. Then look up the meanings in a dictionary and write them on the paper. Share your list with a classmate. Try to use each other's words in sentences.

Name:

Famous People

Name of your newspaper:

Date of your newspaper:

The more you read the newspaper, the more you will be able to recognize people who are often in the news. Search your newspaper to see how many of these pictures or names of important people you can find.

Can You Find?	What's the Name?
• the president of the U.S.A.	__________
• the governor of your state	__________
• a senator	__________
• a European head of state	__________
• an African head of state	__________
• a sports star	__________
• a movie star	__________
• a singer	__________
• a leader in your community	__________
• someone you know	__________

Newspaper Time Line

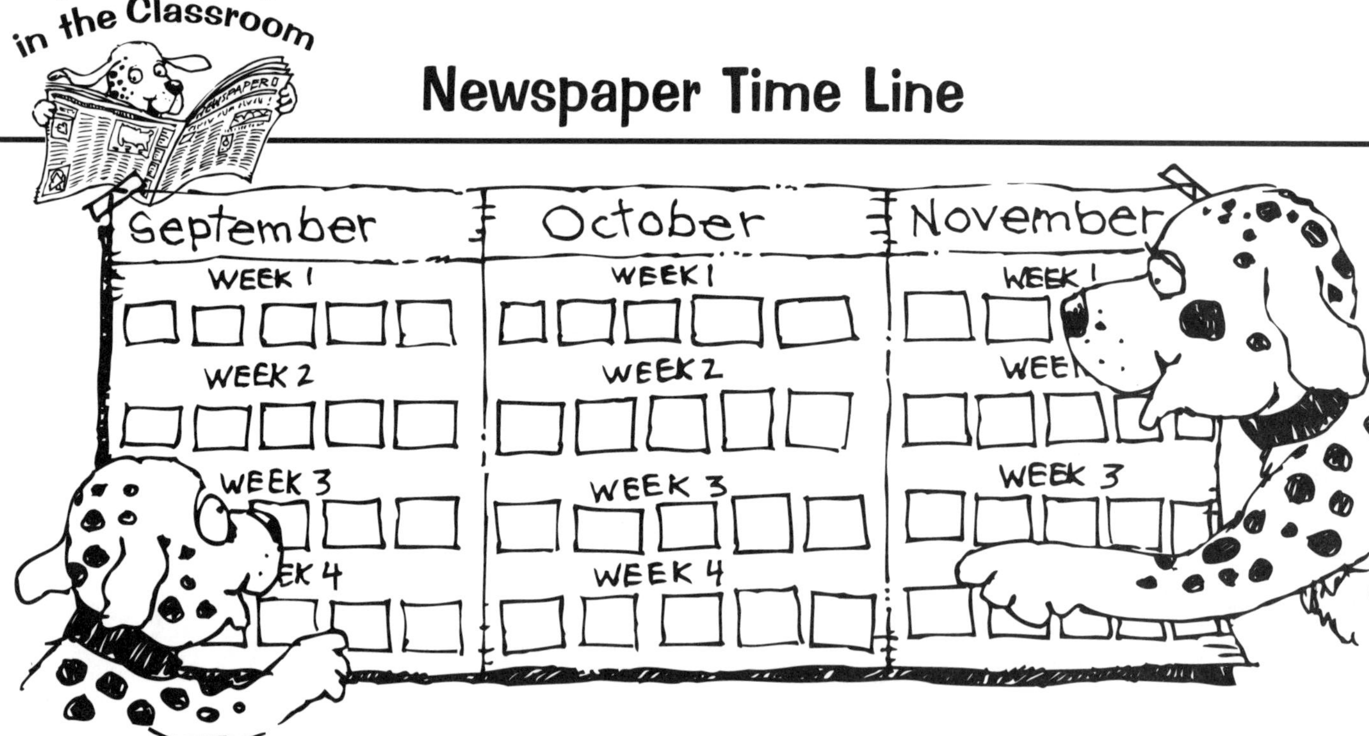

To encourage students to read the newspaper regularly, create a class Newspaper Time Line. Not only will your class be involved in reading the newspaper, but they will end up with an overview of the year's current events. The time line can be used to assist students in understanding causes and effects of certain events, observing trends, and making informed predictions.

Materials

- large roll of butcher paper posted on classroom wall
  (Devote as much space as possible.)
- daily newspapers—one per student is ideal, one per group acceptable
- scissors
- glue or tape
- markers

Steps to Follow

1. Segment the time line by month, beginning with the first month of school. Divide the month into weeks.

2. Appoint committees of three or four students for each of the following areas:
   international news
   national news
   state news
   local news
   sports and/or human interest

3. Each committee will be responsible for selecting what they consider to be the most important news item of the week in their area. They will cut out the headline from the article and place it on the time line.

4. Committee positions may be reassigned on a rotating basis so that each student will have a chance to serve on more than one committee.

Newspaper Journal

If you do not have enough space to display a Newspaper Time Line or you prefer an individual project, ask students to keep a "Newspaper Journal." Journal entries may be made daily or weekly.

- Each student will need a spiral-bound notebook.
- Beginning as soon as possible in the school year, have each student read the newspaper and select one significant article.
- The headline for the article should be cut out and glued into the notebook (or copied if several students are using the same newspaper.) Enter the date also.
- The student will then summarize the article and comment on its importance.

This provides a meaningful journal experience, some good practice in reading and writing, and a wonderful retrospective of the events of the year.

On Your Birthday

In this motivating activity, students create a newspaper front page giving the top stories of the day of their birth. Since this project requires the use of microfiche records, the research aspect is best done as a homework assignment.

- Reproduce the letter below to introduce the assignment to parents.
- Reproduce page 233 for each student.
- Talk to the reference librarian at your local public library beforehand. You may wish to make this assignment to a few students at a time—the librarian will thank you for it!

Conducting the Research

- Students locate and read the articles they find most interesting. They should include international, national, local, and even sports events.
- Students take notes and write a short version (one or two paragraphs) of each story.

Creating the Front Page

- Have students compile their newspaper pages at school.
- Stories are to be written in column form on a sheet of paper, using appropriate headlines.
- Of course, one headline should announce the birth of the student and be followed by a short paragraph giving information about the baby and family. These may be illustrated with baby pictures.
- If you have access to a computer, these newspapers can be given a very authentic look, and students can gain proficiency in word processing and page layout.

Dear Parents:

Your help is needed to enable your child to complete an exciting assignment requiring a trip to the public library.

He/she is to use the library microfiche records to find the newspaper from the day of his/her birth and follow the directions on the "On Your Birthday" instruction sheet.

You can help your child read the newspaper articles and take notes on the important aspects.

The reference librarian is expecting you and will help you get started. Have fun!

Sincerely,

Name:

On Your Birthday 2

You are going to create a newspaper front page that tells the important events of the day of your birth. To do this you will go to the public library and use a special kind of film called **microfiche**. It is a way of keeping newspapers and magazines without having to store the actual paper copy.

Materials

- a pencil
- notecards or notepaper

Steps to Follow

1. With the help of the reference librarian, find the local newspaper from the day of your birth.
2. Look at all the headlines in the paper. Find one that sounds interesting in each of these categories:

   international news

   national news

   local news

   sports news

3. Copy each headline on a separate piece of paper.
4. Read one article.
5. Take notes on what you read. You might write the 5 W's on the paper and answer each W.
6. Read and take notes on each of the other articles.
7. Bring your headlines and notes to school by this date:

HEADLINE

WHO

WHAT

WHERE

WHEN

WHY

Newspapers in the Classroom

The Power of the Pen

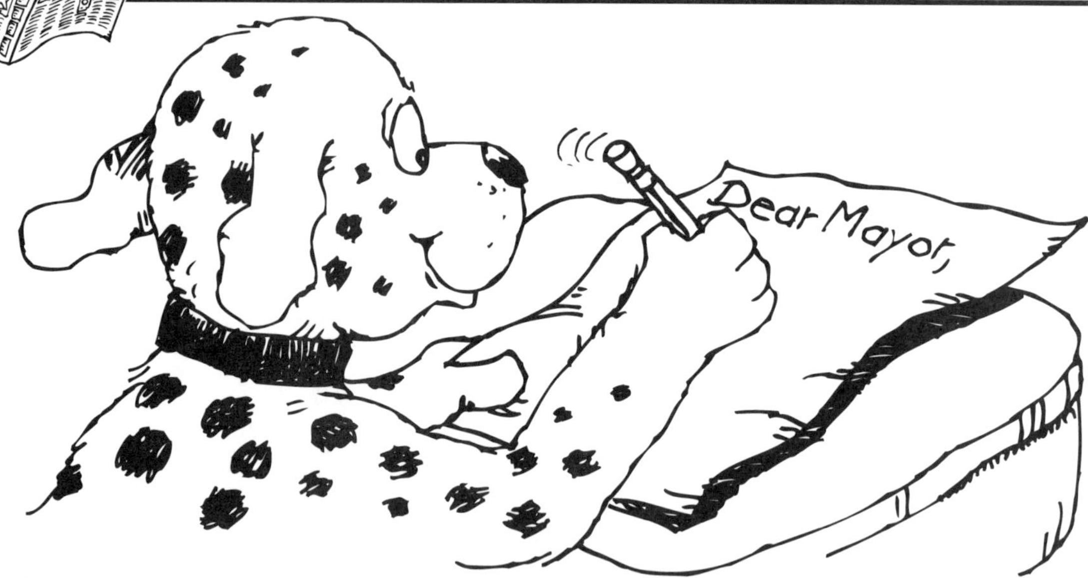

Guide your students in an exploration that will help them understand how individuals can make a difference. Post a chart entitled "Our Cause" in the classroom. As students read the newspaper over a period of several weeks, ask them to record on the chart issues or causes that interest them. After a number of causes have been recorded, hold a class meeting to discuss which one is of greatest interest to the class as a whole.

The next step is to brainstorm to come up with some actions that might be taken on behalf of the cause. Ask questions such as:

> Should the class write letters? If so, to whom?
>
> Would a petition be appropriate?
>
> Could a fundraiser or rally be held?
>
> Should a press release be sent to local news outlets?

As an example, let's say your students decide that they want to see the streets and highways of your community free of litter. They might:

1. Write local government to find out if the "adopt-a-highway" program is available in your community.

2. Then write to business owners and civic groups and ask these parties to adopt a section of highway.

3. Write letters to the editor and government officials.

4. Invite "adopters" to school to make their pledges public and receive a certificate of appreciation.

5. Send a press release and an invitation to the local newspaper or television station in hopes of getting coverage.

   You can be quite sure that students will read the paper if they think they might find themselves in its pages.

While this type of project seems ambitious, it is not really difficult to carry out and gives students many opportunities to strengthen skills in reading, writing, research, communication, and planning.

Create a Class Newspaper

Reading the newspaper on a regular basis may inspire you and your students to start a paper of your own! In the process, students will learn about gathering news and information, improve their writing skills, and perhaps gain insight into the world around them.

Before you begin, students should have experience in reading a daily paper. They should be familiar with the types of information that can be found in the various sections of the newspaper.

Planning the Paper

1. Brainstorm with the students to generate a list of the sections of the newspaper. Write the name of each section as a heading on a large sheet of chart paper. Discuss each section to develop a brief description of its purpose and the kinds of information found in that section. Record these descriptions on the chart papers. (Be sure to include a section for School News.)

2. Discuss with your students the various tasks that must be accomplished in order to produce each section. For instance, the sports page might require the services of reporters to cover the games, commentators to write opinion or "color" pieces about the players, and photographers to provide pictures to go with the stories. The society or people section might need the services of an advice columnist, an astrologer, writers to generate human interest stories, and perhaps cartoonists to create comic strips. Add your list of jobs to each chart.

3. Discuss with students the fact that gathering the information and writing the stories and features for the newspaper is only part of the job. Production of the paper involves selecting which stories will be published (editing) and organizing them in an attractive, readable manner (layout). In addition, people are needed to print, collate, and distribute the newspaper. On an additional chart list these jobs: Editing, Layout, Printing, and Distribution.

4. Look over the charts with your students. Discuss which sections might be most appropriate for your class to include in their paper. Remove the chart for any sections that you do not wish to include in your class paper, at least for the time being. Be sure to save them in case you should decide to expand your coverage as time goes on!

Create a Class Newspaper (continued)

Getting Started

Now, the fun begins. Ask students to look over all the available jobs and choose the one they would most like to have. Some students may wish to share a large job or take on two or three small ones. This will depend, of course, on the number of sections you undertake and the number of students in your class.

Here are some suggestions for getting started with each section.

1. **School news**
   Have your reporters schedule a regular meeting with an administrator to obtain a calendar of upcoming school events and other information.

   Ask your principal if the paper can have a mailbox in the school office where teachers can drop "press releases" about their classroom activities for reporters to pick up.

2. **Community news**
   Establish a contact with your local Chamber of Commerce and/or someone from your local government. Assign a reporter to call on a prearranged, regular basis to obtain information about community news and events.

3. **State, national, and international news**
   Each of these sections will be handled in much the same way. Reporters will have to rely on other news sources to obtain information. Since your newspaper cannot be as current as a daily paper, ask students to write a summary of important recent news events.

4. **Editorial page**
   Have students take turns writing editorial commentary. Be sure to approve each commentary before the paper goes to production! Encourage students from other classes to respond to the editorials and other articles in the paper with "Letters to the Editor." Create a drop box in your classroom or the school office to receive these letters. Encourage one or more students to create political cartoons. Again, be sure they are submitted to you for approval!

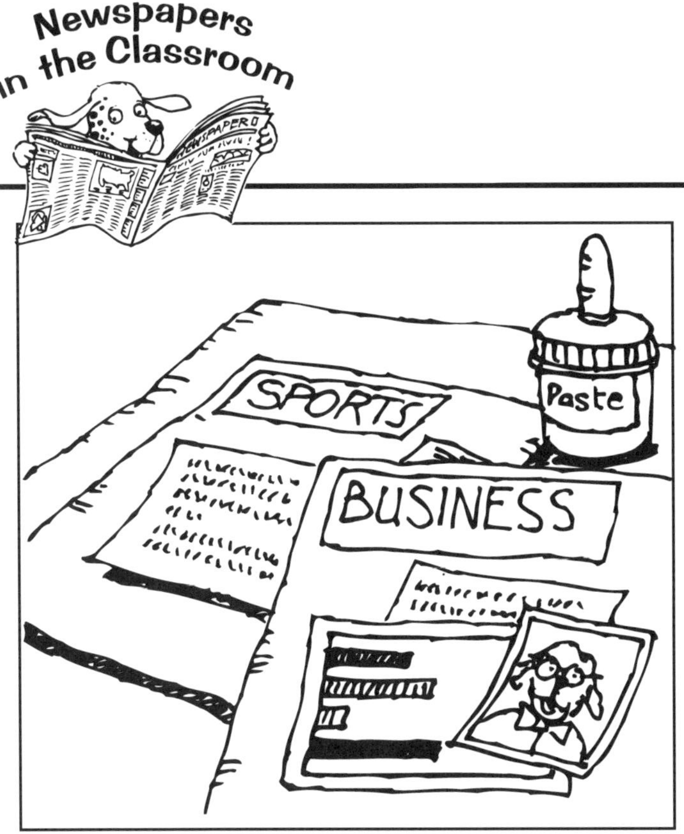

5. Sports
You might wish to cover only local sports events, or allow students to add reports on professional sports by watching televised coverage and reading the print media coverage.

6. Business
If you decide to include this section, suggest that the reporters find a mentor, perhaps a parent or volunteer from the Chamber of Commerce. Possible articles might be how to open a savings account, how to be a smart consumer, what kinds of businesses are in town, and what kind of skills they require of employees.

7. Society/People
Assign reporters to find human interest stories in the school or community. Make sure that you have writers for all features you wish to include, such as advice columns, helpful hints (for studying instead of housework?), crosswords or other word puzzles, and cartoons.

8. Classified ads
Establish a lost and found section, a personal ad section, and a section where teachers, other school personnel, and the PTA can advertise for "Help Wanted."

Examples:

Found: Paperback copy of *Black Beauty.* No name inside. Turned in to office.

Jaime, great improvement in math. Keep up the good work! Mom and Dad.

Baked goods needed for PTA bake sale. Bring to the cafeteria on Wed., Jan. 10.

The office staff would like artistically inclined students to help with bulletin board displays. See Mr. Benson before October 1.

Mrs. Schulze's class is collecting foam egg cartons for a class project. Please bring to Room 4.

Create a Class Newspaper (concluded)

Producing the Paper

The production of the paper will demand a great deal of time and energy from all concerned. If you become concerned about the amount of time that is being devoted to the project, remember that much is being accomplished. Students are practicing the real-life skills of communication, cooperation, and responsibility, along with research, reading, and writing!

1. Decide with your class how often the paper will be published. Monthly publication is generally a realistic goal, especially at the beginning. Older students may be able to increase publication to biweekly or even weekly if they are highly motivated.

2. Set aside a regular time period to work on the paper in class. Check to see if your principal will allow your reporters to make local calls from the school office.

3. Set deadlines for all articles to be completed and turned in to the editors for corrections and approvals. Make it clear that only clean, finished work will be considered for publication. Remind students to have you check work before they submit it.

4. Lay out the newspaper using a word processing program, if available. If you do not have access to a computer and printer, use the cut-and-paste headlines on pages 239 and 240. Paste headlines and articles to a blank sheet of paper in an attractive arrangement.

5. Print your newspaper on a copy machine.

6. Deliver fresh copies of your paper to your readers!

Resources

The printing of the paper can become quite expensive, especially if you strive for a wide circulation. Ask local office supply stores, printers, or even your local newspaper for help with supplies and copying. Other businesses might be happy to make donations in exchange for the publication of small advertisements in your paper.

Here are a few books that might be helpful:

Running a School Newspaper by Vivian Dubrovin; Franklin Watts, 1985.
Deadline! From News to Newspaper by Gail Gibbons; Crowell, 1987.
Behind the Headlines at a Big City Paper by Betty Lou English; Lothrop, Lee & Shepard Books, 1985.
Investigative Reporting by Marilyn Moorcroft; Franklin Watts, 1981.

Cut-and-Paste Headlines

If your class does not have access to a computer, use these cut-and-paste headlines to help give your paper a professional look.

The Messenger

The Schoolview

The Room Crier

The School Bell

THE INDEPENDENT

0 1 2 3 4 5 6 7 8 9

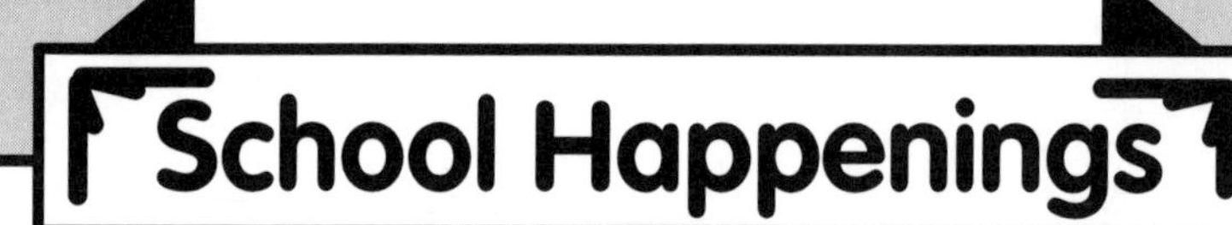

Community News

Our State

National News

Editorial Page

Sports

People and Society

Business News

Classified Ads

Magazines in the Classroom

Magazines can get even hard-to-motivate students reading. Bright, intriguing photographs and interesting subject matter can draw kids into the text.

ACTIVITIES

How to Get Magazines for Your Classroom (Page 242)

Children's Magazines (Page 243)
Here is a partial list of the many fine children's magazines available.

Introducing Magazines to Your Class (Page 244)
Familiarize students with magazine formats and features.

Magazine Covers (Pages 245–247)
Using real magazines or a transparency of the sample provided, students learn about the information found on magazine covers. They then create their own magazine covers and use a checklist to evaluate each other's work.

Magazine Table of Contents (Pages 248–250)
After discussing what can be found in a typical magazine table of contents, students answer questions about the table of contents of a specific magazine.

Magazine Advertisements (Pages 251 and 252)
Use a transparency of a sample ad to discuss how words and pictures are used to try to sell a product. Students then examine and evaluate ads from real magazines.

Reading a Magazine Article (Pages 253–260)
Use the sample article to study the ways in which magazines present information. Students then use real magazines to locate information.

Mystery Picture (Pages 261)

The Whole Picture (Pages 262 and 263)
These activities focus on photographs, illustrations, and captions.

Classroom Literary Magazine (Page 264)
If creating your own literary magazine sounds like fun, here are some tips.

How to Get Magazines for Your Classroom

Before planning to use this section on reading magazines, you will need to plan for a sufficient supply of children's magazines. This requires some advance thought, but it is possible if you aren't afraid to ask others for assistance.

New or Almost-New Magazines

1. The subscription rate to children's periodicals varies from around $20 to $50 per year. If your PTA gives you a yearly monetary gift, what better use for it?

2. If appropriate, you might put magazine subscriptions on the class wish list that you send to parents at the beginning of the year. It's very possible that working parents who can't spend time in the classroom would love to "volunteer" in this manner.

3. Seek subscription donations from businesses you patronize and local service clubs. You may need to write up a formal proposal, but it would be worth it for a "grant" that would buy a number of magazine subscriptions.

4. Students who have personal magazine subscriptions may not save magazines once they have read them. Ask that they bring these "almost new" issues to school.

5. Ask your pediatrician's office for last month's issues.

Used Magazines

Unlike adult news magazines, most of the articles in children's magazines are not "time sensitive." This is great for creating your classroom collection because issues do not need to be current. Where to look?

1. Ask your school librarian if she or he gets rid of magazines at the end of the school year. If so, put "dibs" on those that are appropriate for your students.

2. Talk to the children's librarian at the public library to see what their procedures are for disposing of old magazines. Some libraries may even have a periodic "giveaway day" for teachers.

3. Ask friends and students' parents who are garage sale afficionados to be on the lookout for appropriate periodicals.

A Special Reminder

Several of the projects in this section of the book require cutting pictures from magazines. Please make sure that these projects are done in class so that you can choose and monitor which magazines are used. Public librarians report a high incidence of magazines being defaced by students who have been assigned a "collage" project as homework by a well-intentioned, but unaware, teacher.

Children's Magazines

While "adult" newspapers are fairly readable for intermediate-aged students, many adult magazines are not. Fortunately there are many fine magazines for children. Here is a partial list of the excellent children's magazines appropriate for grades 4 and up. Some focus on a particular subject area; others are eclectic.

1. Cobblestone Publications
   (a division of the *Cricket* Magazine Group)
   www.cobblestonepub.com
   - *Faces* (world cultures and geography)
   - *Cobblestone* (American history)
   - *Calliope* (world history)
   - *Odyssey* (adventures in science)
   - *Muse* (science and discovery)

2. *Cricket* (literary)
   Cricket Magazine Group
   www.cricketmag.com

3. *National Geographic World*
   1-800-647-5463

4. *Ranger Rick*
   National Wildlife Federation
   1-800-611-1599

5. *Stone Soup* (literary)
   www.stonesoup.com
   1-800-447-4569

6. *Sports Illustrated for Kids*
   www.sikids.com
   1-800-833-1661

7. *Archaeology's Dig*
   1-800-225-5344

8. *Kids Discover*
   1-800-825-2821

9. *Boy's Life*
   1-972-580-2088

10. *American Girl*
    1-800-234-1278

11. *Owl*
    (science, technology, the natural world)
    1-800-551-6957

12. *Highlights*
    www.highlights.com

Introducing Magazines to Your Class

What's in a Magazine?

1. Divide the class into groups and give each group a different magazine. Try to use magazines with a variety of content (nature, people, news, literary, general interest, etc.).
2. Instruct each group to list all the general things found in their magazine, for example: photographs, puzzle, table of contents, articles on animals, etc.
3. Compile a class list by having each group in turn tell one thing they found. Groups may not repeat what another group said. Continue until all the group lists have been exhausted.
4. Switch magazines so that each group has a different one.
5. Name an item from the compiled list. If a group finds that item in their magazine, write the name of the magazine next to the item on the list.
6. Evaluate the results by asking questions such as:

   What did we find in every kind of magazine?

   Which magazines have riddles and puzzles?

   Which magazines have (or don't have) advertisements?

   What would be some choices if you wanted to read about animals?

Extension Activity

Play this scavenger hunt game.
You will need a variety of magazines, four to six per group.

1. Divide students into groups of three or four; groups should choose a member to be the recorder.
2. The recorder lists the letters of the alphabet vertically along the left-hand side of a sheet of lined paper. (Skip a line between letters.)
3. Groups are to locate the name of a person, place, thing, or an event (not advertisements) that begins with each letter of the alphabet.
4. Then they use the information given in the article to write a sentence about the item, underlining the alphabetical item. An entry might look like this:

A Australia
Australia has been enduring a terrible drought for several years.
B

Magazine Covers

A magazine's cover is the feature that attracts readers. Publishers put large amounts of time and resources into cover design. In this activity, students will learn about the information found on magazine covers. They then create their own magazine covers and use a checklist to evaluate each other's work.

Materials

- overhead transparency of sample cover on page 246
- cover checklist on page 247, reproduced for each student
- real magazines
- drawing paper
- crayons and/or marking pens

page 246

page 247

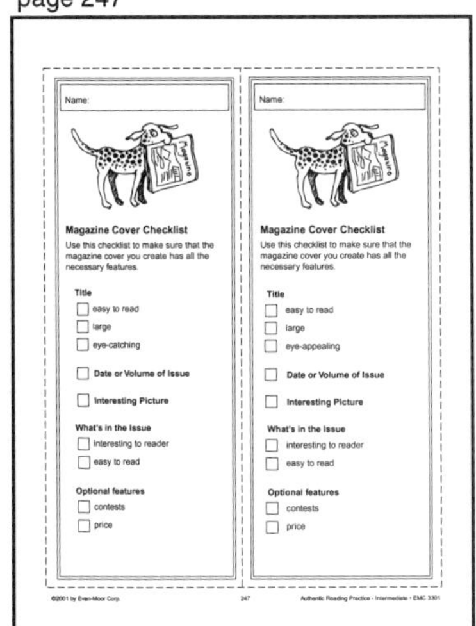
Name:

Magazine Cover Checklist

Use this checklist to make sure that the magazine cover you create has all the necessary features.

Title
- [ ] easy to read
- [ ] large
- [ ] eye-catching

- [ ] Date or Volume of Issue
- [ ] Interesting Picture

What's in the Issue
- [ ] interesting to reader
- [ ] easy to read

Optional features
- [ ] contests
- [ ] price

Steps to Follow

1. View the transparency of the sample cover and ask questions such as:

   What is the name of the magazine?

   What kinds of articles are in this issue?

   Is there a contest of some kind? What could you win?

   What does the cover have that makes you want to read the issue?

   What other information is found on the cover?

2. Make a list of the standard information one would expect to find on a magazine cover.
3. Have students create a cover that utilizes all the aspects on the list. You may want to give them "free rein" or have them draw a magazine type "from a hat" (science, sports, news, television guide, computer, etc.).
4. Students evaluate each other's covers, using the checklist on page 247.

Sample Magazine Cover

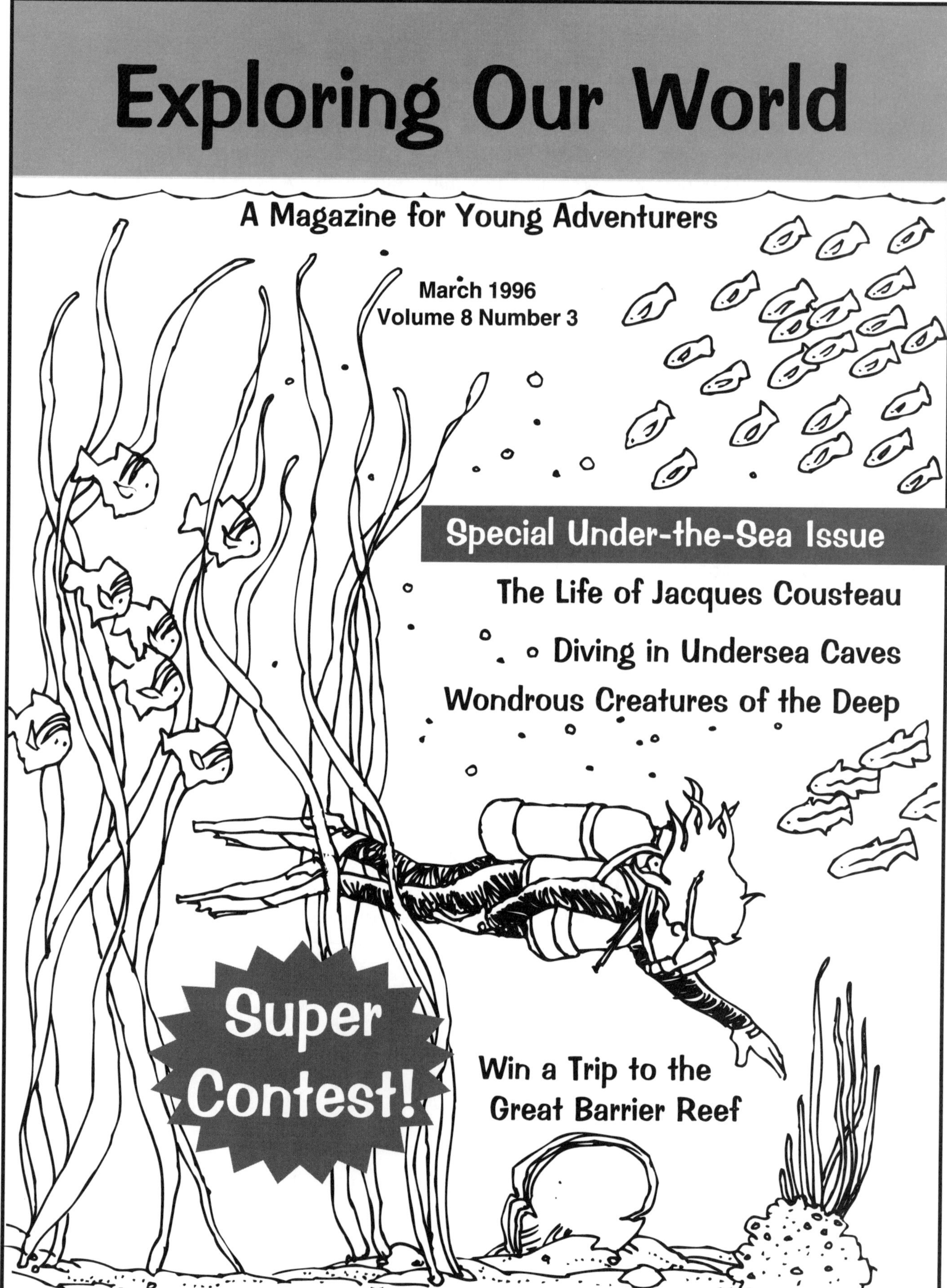

Name:

Magazine Cover Checklist

Use this checklist to make sure that the magazine cover you create has all the necessary features.

Title

- ☐ easy to read
- ☐ large
- ☐ eye-catching

☐ **Date or Volume of Issue**

☐ **Interesting Picture**

What's in the Issue

- ☐ interesting to reader
- ☐ easy to read

Optional features

- ☐ contests
- ☐ price

Name:

Magazine Cover Checklist

Use this checklist to make sure that the magazine cover you create has all the necessary features.

Title

- ☐ easy to read
- ☐ large
- ☐ eye-catching

☐ **Date or Volume of Issue**

☐ **Interesting Picture**

What's in the Issue

- ☐ interesting to reader
- ☐ easy to read

Optional features

- ☐ contests
- ☐ price

Magazine Table of Contents

Materials

- overhead transparency of sample table of contents on page 249
- questionnaire on page 250, reproduced for each student
- children's magazines or photocopies of several tables of contents

Steps to Follow

1. View the transparency of the sample table of contents and ask questions such as:

   Where can you find out what the photograph on the cover shows?

   Are there things other than articles in this issue? What are they?

   What does the magazine include on the contents page to generate interest?

   On what page would you look to find…?

2. Supply each student with a copy of page 250 and a children's magazine or photocopied table of contents.
3. Students answer the questions using the table of contents they were given.
4. Trade magazines and questionnaires to check each other's comprehension.

page 249

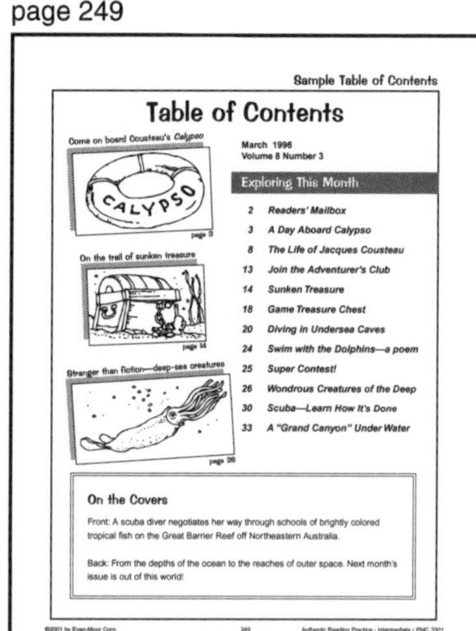
Sample Table of Contents

Table of Contents

Come on board Cousteau's *Calypso* — page 3

On the trail of sunken treasure — page 14

Stranger than fiction—deep-sea creatures — page 26

March 1996
Volume 8 Number 3

Exploring This Month

2 *Readers' Mailbox*
3 *A Day Aboard Calypso*
8 *The Life of Jacques Cousteau*
13 *Join the Adventurer's Club*
14 *Sunken Treasure*
18 *Game Treasure Chest*
20 *Diving in Undersea Caves*
24 *Swim with the Dolphins—a poem*
25 *Super Contest!*
26 *Wondrous Creatures of the Deep*
30 *Scuba—Learn How It's Done*
33 *A "Grand Canyon" Under Water*

On the Covers

Front: A scuba diver negotiates her way through schools of brightly colored tropical fish on the Great Barrier Reef off Northeastern Australia.

Back: From the depths of the ocean to the reaches of outer space. Next month's issue is out of this world!

©2001 by Evan-Moor Corp. 249 Authentic Reading Practice - Intermediate • EMC 3301

page 250

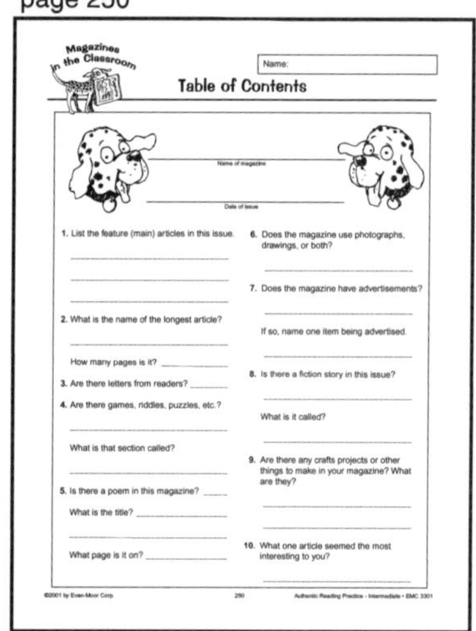
Magazines in the Classroom

Name:

Table of Contents

Name of magazine

Date of issue

1. List the feature (main) articles in this issue.
2. What is the name of the longest article?
   How many pages is it? ______
3. Are there letters from readers? ______
4. Are there games, riddles, puzzles, etc.?
   What is that section called?
5. Is there a poem in this magazine? ______
   What is the title? ______
   What page is it on? ______
6. Does the magazine use photographs, drawings, or both?
7. Does the magazine have advertisements?
   If so, name one item being advertised.
8. Is there a fiction story in this issue?
   What is it called?
9. Are there any crafts projects or other things to make in your magazine? What are they?
10. What one article seemed the most interesting to you?

©2001 by Evan-Moor Corp. 250 Authentic Reading Practice - Intermediate • EMC 3301

Table of Contents

Come on board Cousteau's *Calypso*

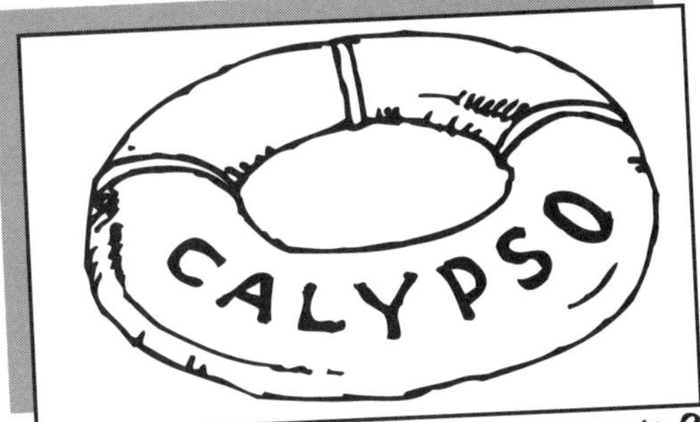

page 3

On the trail of sunken treasure

page 14

Stranger than fiction—deep-sea creatures

page 26

March 1996
Volume 8 Number 3

Exploring This Month

On the Covers

Front: A scuba diver negotiates her way through schools of brightly colored tropical fish on the Great Barrier Reef off Northeastern Australia.

Back: From the depths of the ocean to the reaches of outer space. Next month's issue is out of this world!

Name:

Magazine Table of Contents 2

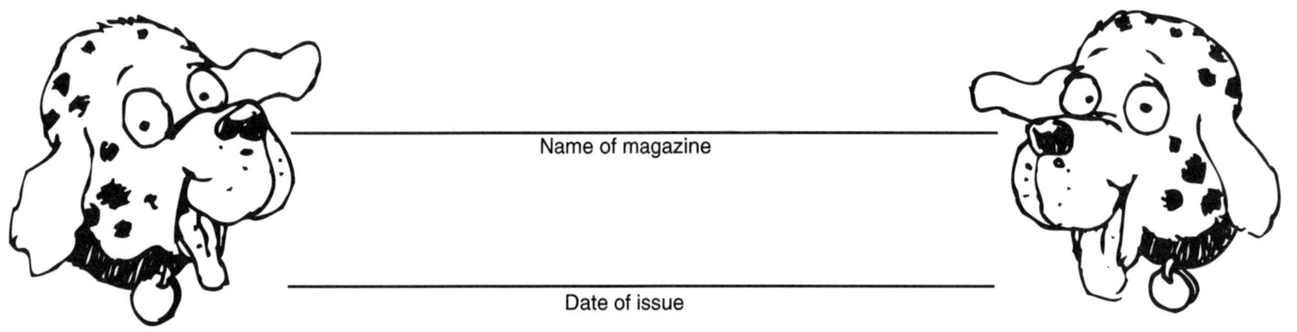

Name of magazine

Date of issue

1. List the feature (main) articles in this issue.

2. What is the name of the longest article?

   How many pages is it?

3. Are there letters from readers?

4. Are there games, riddles, puzzles, etc.?

   What is that section called?

5. Is there a poem in this magazine?

   What is the title?

   What page is it on?

6. Does the magazine use photographs, drawings, or both?

7. Does the magazine have advertisements?

   If so, name one item being advertised.

8. Is there a fiction story in this issue?

   What is it called?

9. Are there any crafts projects or other things to make in your magazine? What are they?

10. What one article seemed the most interesting to you?

Magazine Advertisements

Although most children's magazines that you find in a school setting contain no advertising, many "newsstand" children's magazines do.

Materials

- assortment of child-appropriate magazine ads
- overhead transparency of page 252

page 252

Sample Magazine Advertisement

Cool-Foot® Sneakers
Look Cool!
Be Cool!

Steps to Follow

1. Show several advertisements. Explain that companies that make the products pay the magazines to publish their ads. This is one of the ways the magazines make money. Ask:

   Why do you think companies put ads in magazines?

   Have you or members of your family ever bought something you saw in a magazine advertisement?

2. View the transparency of the sample ad. Discuss how words and pictures are used to try to sell the product. Ask questions such as:

   What is this advertisement trying to sell you?

   What words are used to get you to think this is a good product?

   Why do you think someone might decide to buy this product?

3. Divide students into small groups and give each group several ads. Instruct groups to list all the words used to make someone want to buy the product.
4. Have each group decide which of the ads they viewed is the most effective and present the ad to the class, explaining why they think it is an effective ad.
5. Compile a class list of powerful advertising words.

Cool-Foot® Sneakers

Look Cool! Be Cool!

Reading a Magazine Article

These activities introduce students to the ways a magazine makes information more accessible to its readers.

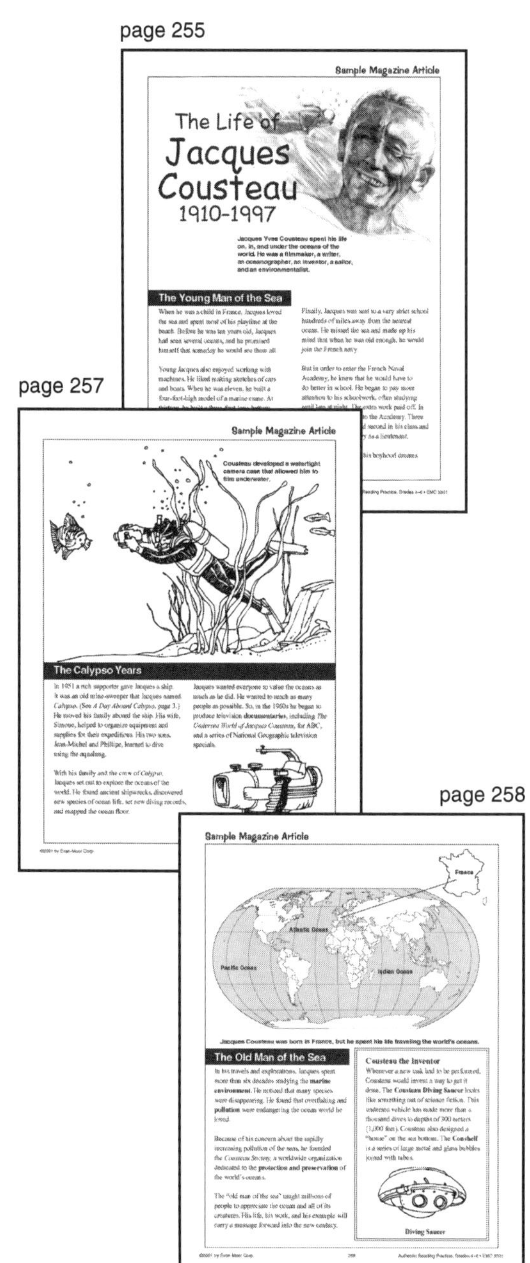

Materials

- sample article on pages 255–258, reproduced for each student
- pages 259 and 260, reproduced for students
- assortment of children's magazines

Steps to Follow

Explain to students that magazines use certain format features to make it easier for readers to find information. List the following "reader helpers" on the chalkboard and discuss them one at a time using the sample article:

- headings
- captions
- key words
- maps, charts, and diagrams
- sidebars (boxed inserts)

Headings

Explain that headings in an article give an overview of what the article will cover. Read the headings in "The Life of Jacques Cousteau" and discuss the kind of information apt to be found under each. Ask questions such as:

> Which section of the article would tell you about life on the *Calypso*?
>
> Could you find out about Cousteau's schooling in the section entitled "The Old Man of the Sea"?

Ask specific questions about the article and have students tell what section they would look in for the information. Read that section to determine if the answer is there.

Reading a Magazine Article (continued)

Captions
If necessary, explain that captions are the words under a picture, map, or diagram, etc. Captions frequently contain important facts. Read the captions in the sample article and discuss the information contained in them.

Key Words
Explain that magazines may use bold or italic type for important words. Have students find these key words in the sample article. Discuss how these words might help the reader locate the information needed to answer a specific question.

Maps and Diagrams
Study the diagram of scuba gear on page 256 and the map on page 258. What information is presented in each? What advantages do these graphics have over information presented in paragraph form?

Sidebars
Information that is related to an article, but does not fit with the flow of the text is often placed in a sidebar. Sidebars are frequently boxed or placed on a colored background to show that they are not part of the main article. Point out "Cousteau the Inventor" on page 258 and explain the use of a sidebar.

Follow-Up

1. Divide students into groups of four. Give each group four different magazines and a copy of page 259. Instruct students to compare the way information is presented in those four magazines.

2. Have individual students read an informational article and, using a copy of page 260, write four questions about the information that utilize the different reader helpers. Then have students exchange magazines and question sheets with one another. Each reads the article, answers the four questions, and indicates what feature aided in locating the needed information.

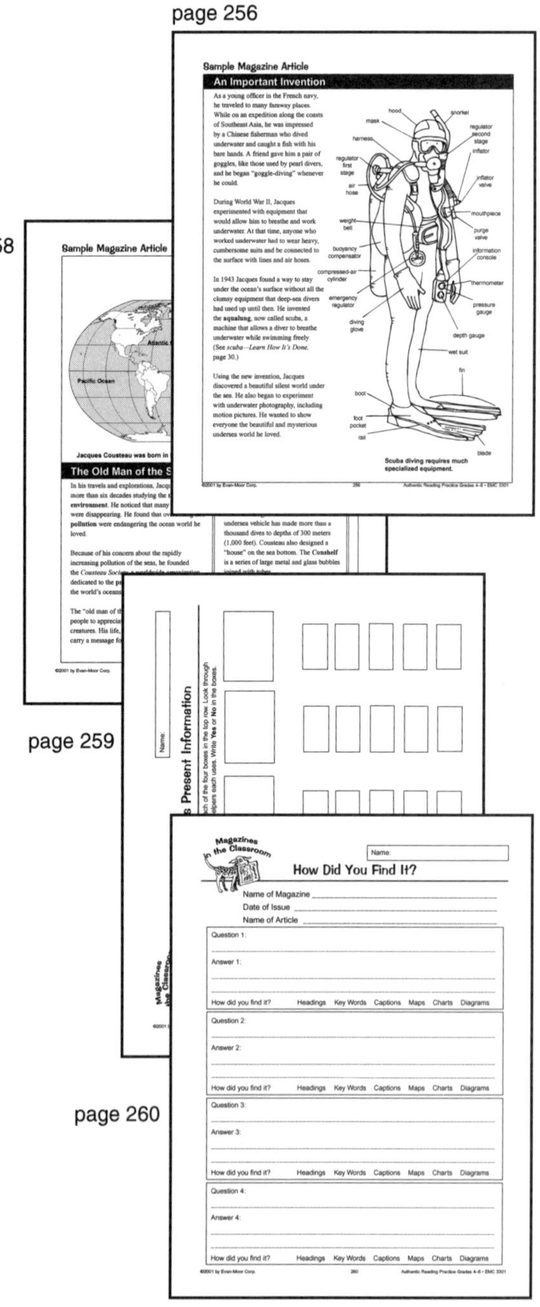
page 256

Sample Magazine Article

An Important Invention

As a young officer in the French navy, he traveled to many faraway places. While on an expedition along the coasts of Southeast Asia, he was impressed by a Chinese fisherman who dived underwater and caught a fish with his bare hands. A friend gave him a pair of goggles, like those used by pearl divers, and he began "goggle-diving" whenever he could.

During World War II, Jacques experimented with equipment that would allow him to breathe and work underwater. At that time, anyone who worked underwater had to wear heavy, cumbersome suits and be connected to the surface with lines and air hoses.

In 1943 Jacques found a way to stay under the ocean's surface without all the clumsy equipment that deep-sea divers had used up until then. He invented the **aqualung**, now called scuba, a machine that allows a diver to breathe underwater while swimming freely. (See *scuba—Learn How It's Done*, page 30.)

Using the new invention, Jacques discovered a beautiful silent world under the sea. He also began to experiment with underwater photography, including motion pictures. He wanted to show everyone the beautiful and mysterious undersea world he loved.

Scuba diving requires much specialized equipment.

page 258

Sample Magazine Article

The Old Man of the S

page 259

page 260

How Did You Find It?

Name:

Name of Magazine
Date of Issue
Name of Article

Question 1:
Answer 1:
How did you find it? Headings Key Words Captions Maps Charts Diagrams

Question 2:
Answer 2:
How did you find it? Headings Key Words Captions Maps Charts Diagrams

Question 3:
Answer 3:
How did you find it? Headings Key Words Captions Maps Charts Diagrams

Question 4:
Answer 4:
How did you find it? Headings Key Words Captions Maps Charts Diagrams

The Life of Jacques Cousteau 1910–1997

Jacques Yves Cousteau spent his life on, in, and under the oceans of the world. He was a filmmaker, a writer, an oceanographer, an inventor, a sailor, and an environmentalist.

The Young Man of the Sea

When he was a child in France, Jacques loved the sea and spent most of his playtime at the beach. Before he was ten years old, Jacques had seen several oceans, and he promised himself that someday he would see them all.

Young Jacques also enjoyed working with machines. He liked making sketches of cars and boats. When he was eleven, he built a four-foot-high model of a marine crane. At thirteen, he built a three-foot-long battery-powered automobile.

But though he was smart and interested in all sorts of different things, he did not do well in school. He was bored and got into trouble often.

Finally, Jacques was sent to a very strict school hundreds of miles away from the nearest ocean. He missed the sea and made up his mind that when he was old enough, he would join the French navy.

But in order to enter the French Naval Academy, he knew that he would have to do better in school. He began to pay more attention to his schoolwork, often studying until late at night. The extra work paid off. In 1930 he was admitted to the Academy. Three years later he graduated second in his class and entered the French navy as a lieutenant.

He was ready to make his boyhood dreams come true.

Sample Magazine Article

An Important Invention

As a young officer in the French navy, he traveled to many faraway places. While on an expedition along the coasts of Southeast Asia, he was impressed by a Chinese fisherman who dived underwater and caught a fish with his bare hands. A friend gave him a pair of goggles, like those used by pearl divers, and he began "goggle-diving" whenever he could.

During World War II, Jacques experimented with equipment that would allow him to breathe and work underwater. At that time, anyone who worked underwater had to wear heavy, cumbersome suits and be connected to the surface with lines and air hoses.

In 1943 Jacques found a way to stay under the ocean's surface without all the clumsy equipment that deep-sea divers had used up until then. He invented the **aqualung**, now called scuba, a machine that allows a diver to breathe underwater while swimming freely. (See *Scuba—Learn How It's Done,* page 30.)

Using the new invention, Jacques discovered a beautiful silent world under the sea. He also began to experiment with underwater photography, including motion pictures. He wanted to show everyone the beautiful and mysterious undersea world he loved.

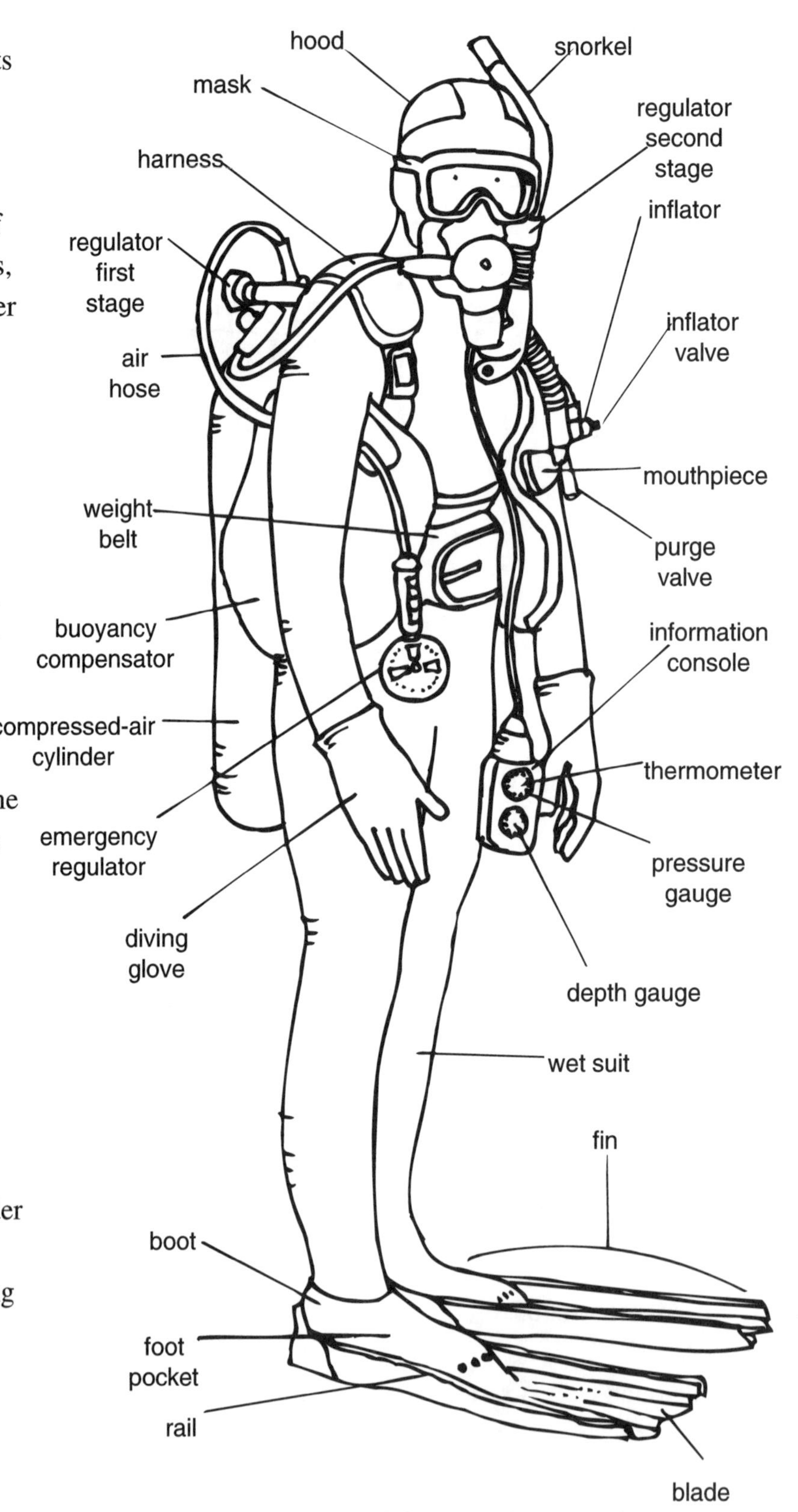

Scuba diving requires much specialized equipment.

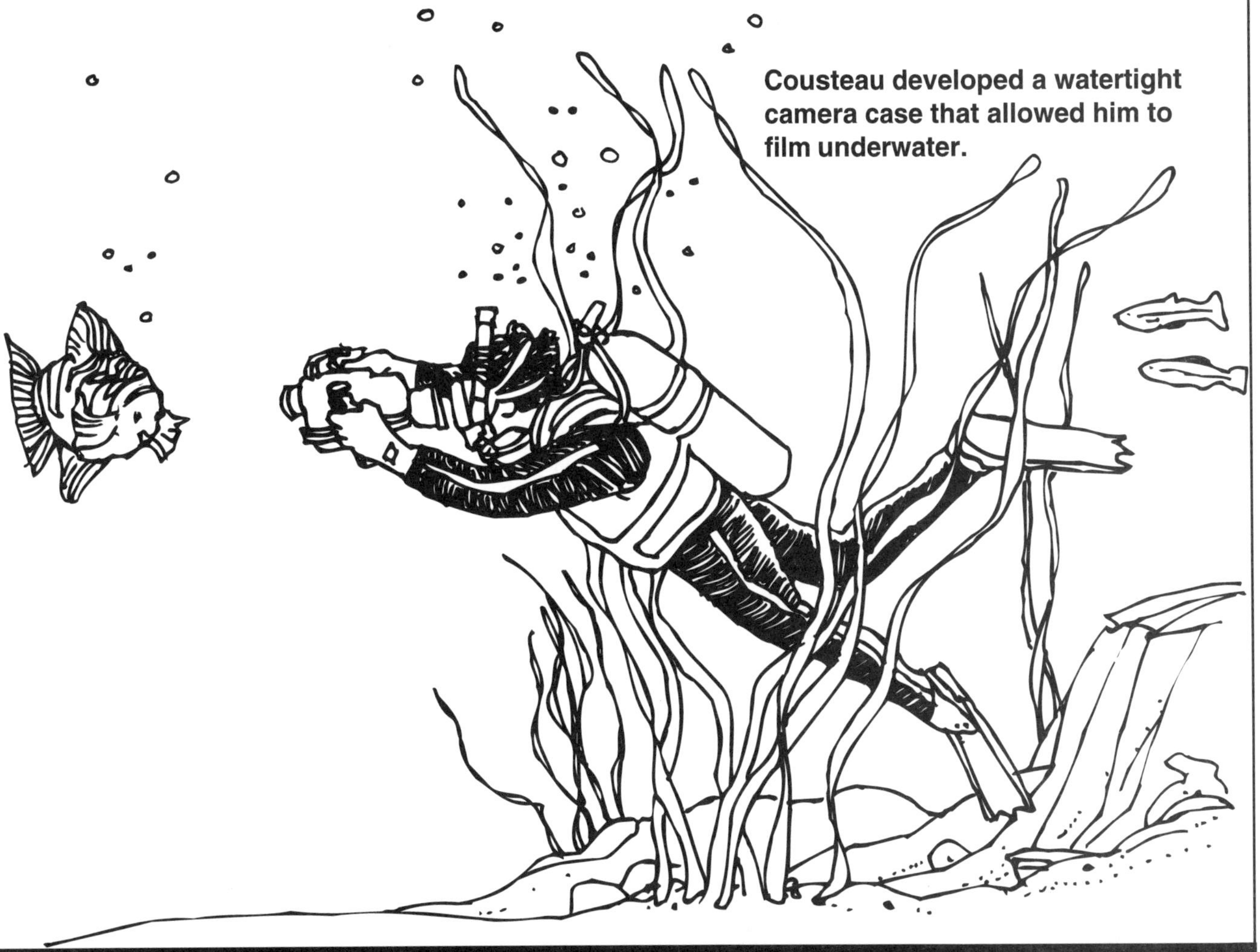

Cousteau developed a watertight camera case that allowed him to film underwater.

The Calypso Years

In 1951 a rich supporter gave Jacques a ship. It was an old mine-sweeper that Jacques named *Calypso*. (See *A Day Aboard Calypso*, page 3.) He moved his family aboard the ship. His wife, Simone, helped to organize equipment and supplies for their expeditions. His two sons, Jean-Michel and Phillipe, learned to dive using the aqualung.

With his family and the crew of *Calypso,* Jacques set out to explore the oceans of the world. He found ancient shipwrecks, discovered new species of ocean life, set new diving records, and mapped the ocean floor.

Jacques wanted everyone to value the oceans as much as he did. He wanted to reach as many people as possible. So, in the 1960s he began to produce television **documentaries**, including *The Undersea World of Jacques Cousteau*, for ABC, and a series of National Geographic television specials.

underwater camera case

Sample Magazine Article

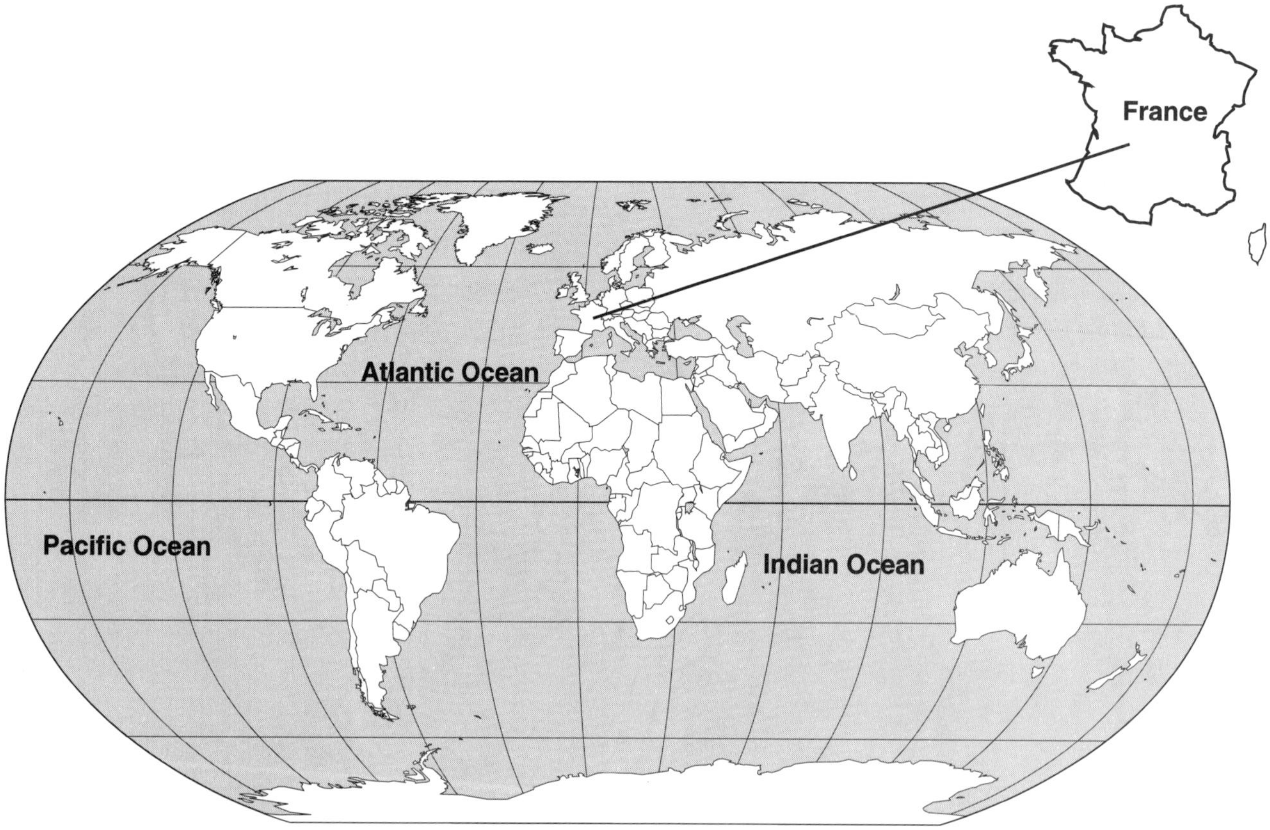

France

Atlantic Ocean

Pacific Ocean

Indian Ocean

Jacques Cousteau was born in France, but he spent his life traveling the world's oceans.

The Old Man of the Sea

In his travels and explorations, Jacques spent more than six decades studying the **marine environment**. He noticed that many species were disappearing. He found that overfishing and **pollution** were endangering the ocean world he loved.

Because of his concern about the rapidly increasing pollution of the seas, he founded the *Cousteau Society,* a worldwide organization dedicated to the **protection and preservation** of the world's oceans.

The "old man of the sea" taught millions of people to appreciate the ocean and all of its creatures. His life, his work, and his example will carry a message forward into the new century.

Cousteau the Inventor

Whenever a new task had to be performed, Cousteau would invent a way to get it done. The **Cousteau Diving Saucer** looks like something out of science fiction. This undersea vehicle has made more than a thousand dives to depths of 300 meters (1,000 feet). Cousteau also designed a "house" on the sea bottom. The **Conshelf** is a series of large metal and glass bubbles joined with tubes.

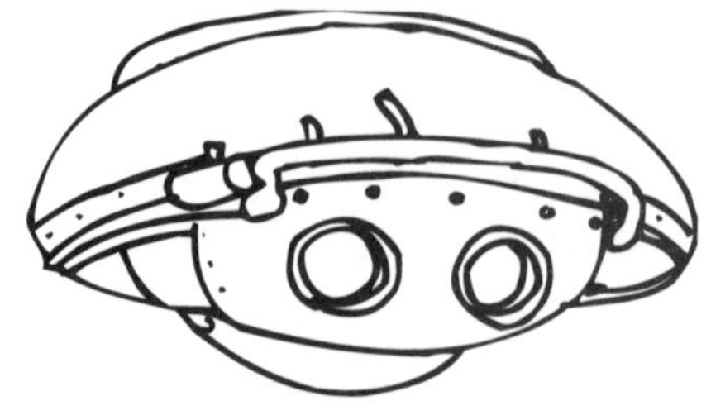

Diving Saucer

Magazines in the Classroom

Name:

How Magazine Articles Present Information

Write the name of a different magazine in each of the four boxes in the top row. Look through each magazine to see which of the reader helpers each uses. Write **Yes** or **No** in the boxes.

Name of Magazine				
Reader Helpers (ways of telling information)				
Section Headings				
Key Words (special type)				
Maps				
Charts/Diagrams				
Sidebars				

Name: ______________________

How Did You Find It?

Name of Magazine ______________________

Date of Issue ______________________

Name of Article ______________________

Question 1:

____

Answer 1:

____

____

How did you find it? Headings Key Words Captions Maps Charts Diagrams

Question 2:

____

Answer 2:

____

____

How did you find it? Headings Key Words Captions Maps Charts Diagrams

Question 3:

____

Answer 3:

____

____

How did you find it? Headings Key Words Captions Maps Charts Diagrams

Question 4:

____

Answer 4:

____

____

How did you find it? Headings Key Words Captions Maps Charts Diagrams

Mystery Picture

This visually interesting project helps students focus on the value of photographs in magazines and then practice writing captions that detail the important aspects of the picture.

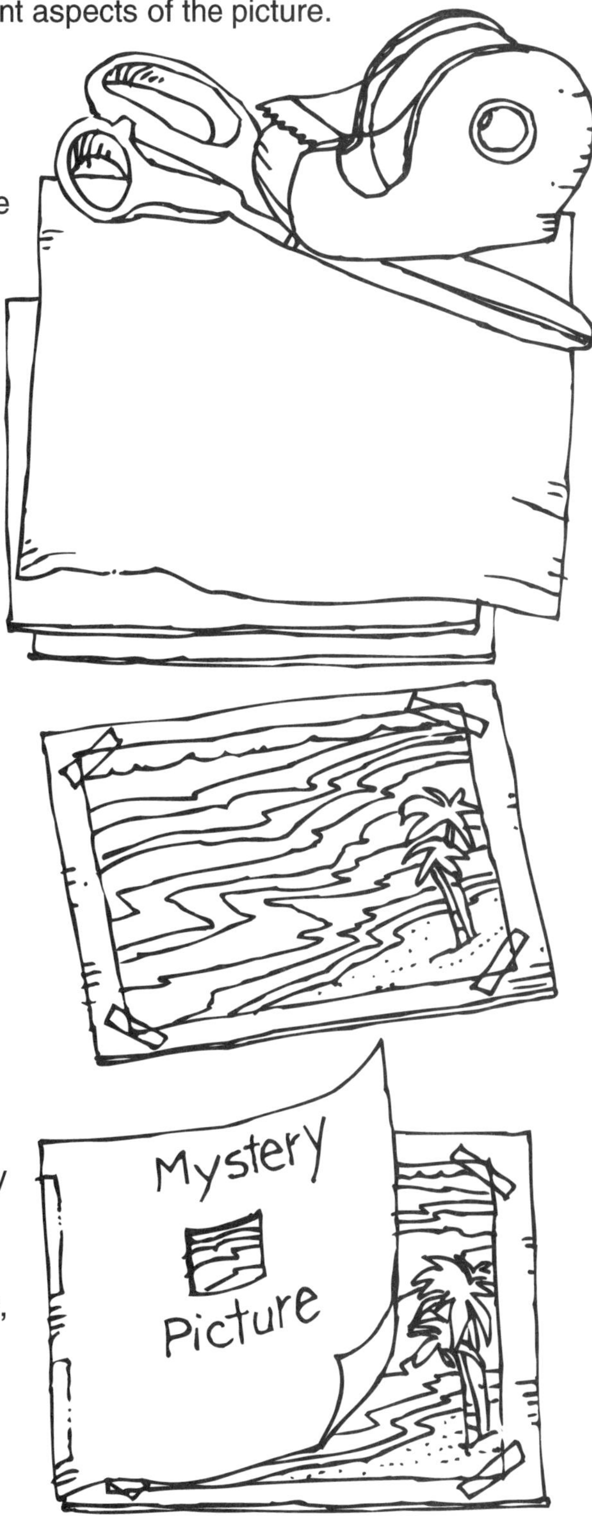

Materials

- variety of magazine pictures, at least 5" x 7" (13 x 18 cm) in size. (The larger the better.)
- construction paper cut slightly larger than the picture
- index cards
- scissors
- tape

Steps to Follow

1. Students select an interesting picture (not an advertisement).
2. Cut a 1" x 1" (2.5 x 2.5 cm) opening in the construction paper cover. The opening should be cut so that it shows some significant portion of the picture without revealing completely what the picture is about.
3. Tape the cover in place so that the desired portion of the picture is visible, but the cover can be lifted to reveal the whole picture.
4. Direct students to write a sentence or two explaining what the picture is about. These explanations should be written on index cards and taped to the back of the picture.

How to Use

1. Number all the mystery pictures and place them in a file at a center.
2. Students must look at the mystery pictures created by their classmates and try to guess, by looking at the portion in the window, what the picture is about.
3. Students record their guesses in complete sentences, numbering their responses to match the pictures. When a student has written a guess about each picture, he or she can look at the whole picture and read the explanation on the back to check his or her guesses.

The Whole Picture

Generate interest in magazines and create an intriguing bulletin board display with this activity. Discuss the importance of magazine photographs and illustrations in communicating the main idea of the article to the reader.

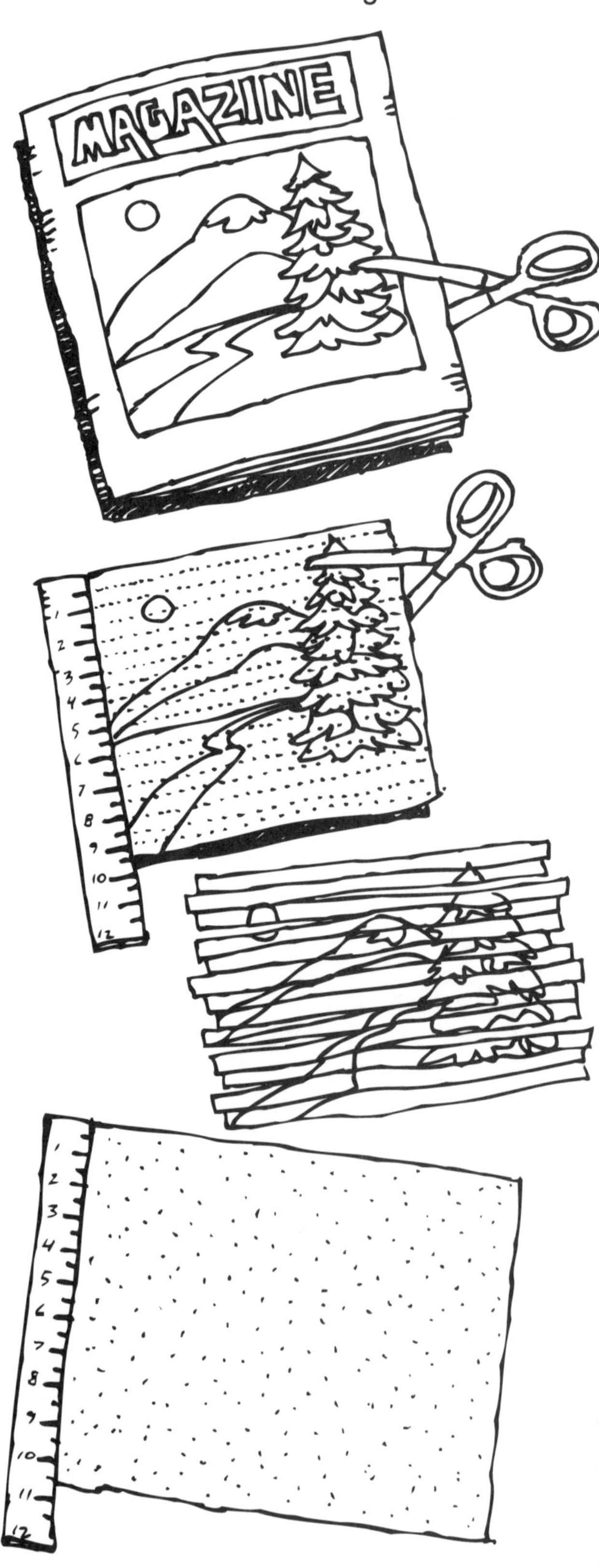

Materials

- magazines with interesting articles and colorful pictures. (Note: Pictures will be cut out of the magazines for this project, so be sure magazines are expendable!)
- 9" x 12" (23 x 30.5 cm) black construction paper
- ruler
- scissors
- white glue

Steps to Follow

1. Students select a magazine article to read.

   An easy way to distribute magazines is to create five or six magazine "stations" around the room. Permit 10 to 12 students at a time to move to stations to select a magazine. Once everyone has chosen a magazine, allow students to return to stations as needed to exchange magazines until all have found one they like. With several stations available, there should be no problem with crowding or confusion.
2. Students choose a picture illustrating the article read. The picture needs to be at least 6" x 8" (15 x 20 cm) in size.
3. Carefully cut out the picture from the magazine. Trim to dimensions that measure to the nearest half-inch.
4. On the back of the picture, rule lines 1/2" (1.25 cm) apart along the length of the picture. Cut the picture apart along these lines as neatly and as carefully as possible. Set aside.
5. Cut a piece of black construction paper 1" (2.5 cm) wider and longer than the picture.

6. Rule a line on the black construction paper 1/2" from a long edge to form a border. Turn the paper and rule lines 1/2" apart all across the width of the paper from the border to the opposite edge.

   Carefully cut along these lines from the edge but STOP at the border.

7. Lay out the strips of the picture in order so that the picture is formed correctly. Beginning with the strip that forms one long edge of the picture, weave over and under the strips of the black paper. Slide the picture strip down next to the border on the black paper. Allow the first black strip to serve as a border on that edge.

8. Begin weaving with the next black strip. Be sure to alternate as you weave. For example, if the first picture strip is placed <u>under</u> the first black weaving strip, the second picture strip should go <u>over</u> the first black weaving strip.

9. Continue weaving until all strips have been used. Make sure all are lined up properly. Use a small dot of glue to secure the ends of all strips. A length of tape on the back of the cut edge of the black paper will strengthen the project.

10. The finished product will resemble a checkerboard with only half of the area of the picture visible. This makes a very intriguing display.

11. Direct each student to write a paragraph using information from the magazine article to explain what is happening in the picture. The paragraph must express the main idea of the article (the whole picture).

12. Mount on a bulletin board labeled "The Whole Picture" or bind into a class book with the same title.

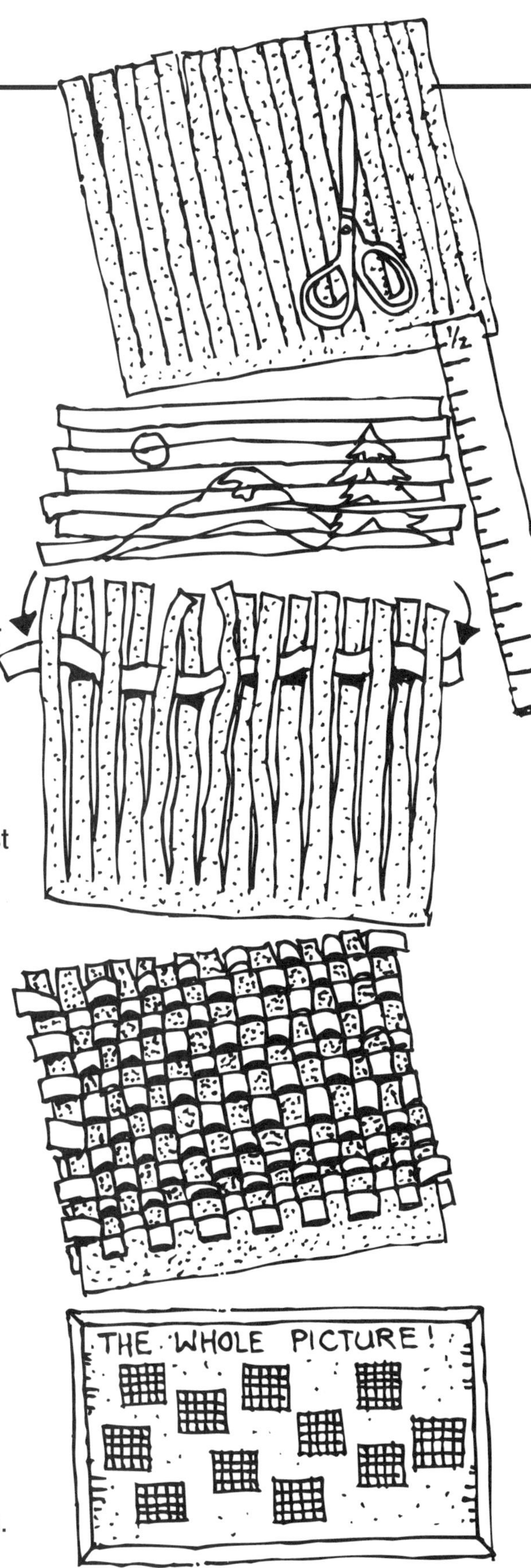

Classroom Literary Magazine

Students will take pride in creating a classroom literary magazine modeled after a real magazine such as *Cricket.*

Planning

1. Gather enough copies of one or more literary magazines so that small groups of three or four students can have a copy of each.
2. Assign the groups to study their magazines and compile a list of the features.
3. Share the groups' findings and compile a class list. Features mentioned should include stories, poems, illustrations and photographs, table of contents, and editorial information such as staff, publication schedule, and how to subscribe.
4. Generate ideas about how to produce a class literary magazine by asking:
   What should the contents include?
   What will the magazine be called?
   What different types of jobs will be required? (storywriters, poets, illustrators, editors, layout and production staff, printers)
   What are the duties of each type of job?
   How many students will be required for each type of job?

Execution

1. Let students sign up for the role each would like to fill. Meet with groups with like roles to discuss how to proceed. Set up guidelines for each group's task.
2. Present the results of the groups' meetings to the entire class and establish dates for various aspects of the magazine to be completed. (If possible, require that submissions be prepared on a word processor.)
3. Meet with each role group as they perform their tasks to provide guidance and answer questions.

Publication

1. Make several photocopies (color for those pages that use color) of the collection and bind them.
2. Present one copy to the school library. Keep the others in the classroom to be enjoyed by all students. Make these available for checkout, as students will want to share their work with their families.

Bonus Activities

In this section you will find a number of extension activities that can relate to either newspapers or magazines. Some are appropriate for homework assignments, and others for center activities. *Biographical Profile* and *A Real Role Model* lend themselves to oral presentations as well.

ACTIVITIES

Word Search

Look through a newspaper or magazine to find certain types of words. Cut them out and glue them to a large sheet of paper in the shape of a triangle. Here's how:

- Place the 1 compound word at the top.
- Place the 2 contractions on the next line.
- Line 3 will have 3 adjectives.
- And so on, with the 10 names of places forming the base of the triangle.

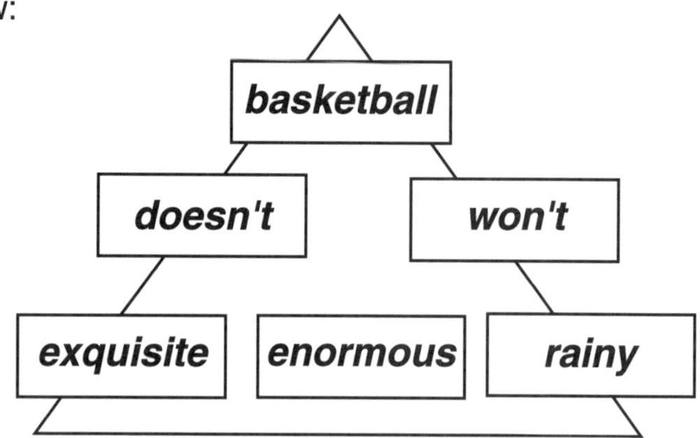

Find **1** compound word.

Find **2** contractions.

Find **3** adjectives.

Find **4** action verbs.

Find **5** three-syllable words.

Find **3 pairs** of synonyms (total 6 words).

Find **7** two-syllable words.

Find **4 pairs** of antonyms (total 8 words).

Find **9** proper nouns that are names of people.

Find **10** proper nouns that are names of places.

Biographical Profile

In this activity, students will use newspaper and magazine articles to construct a poster of a person in the news.

Discuss with the class a number of people who are frequently in the public eye. You may wish to require students to choose someone who has made a positive contribution to his or her field.

Materials

- posterboard
- news magazines, newspapers
- scissors
- glue
- markers

Steps to Follow

1. Students find a photograph showing the person in profile and then use this picture to draw a profile of the person on the posterboard. Make the profiles as large as possible. If students cannot find a profile of their person, they may create a generic profile on their poster.

2. Cut out the profile and set it aside.

3. Next, students search magazines and newspapers to find articles and photographs of the person. These are cut out and mounted, collage fashion, over the entire surface of the profile.

4. Use markers to add the person's name and phrases or sentences that add interest and information.

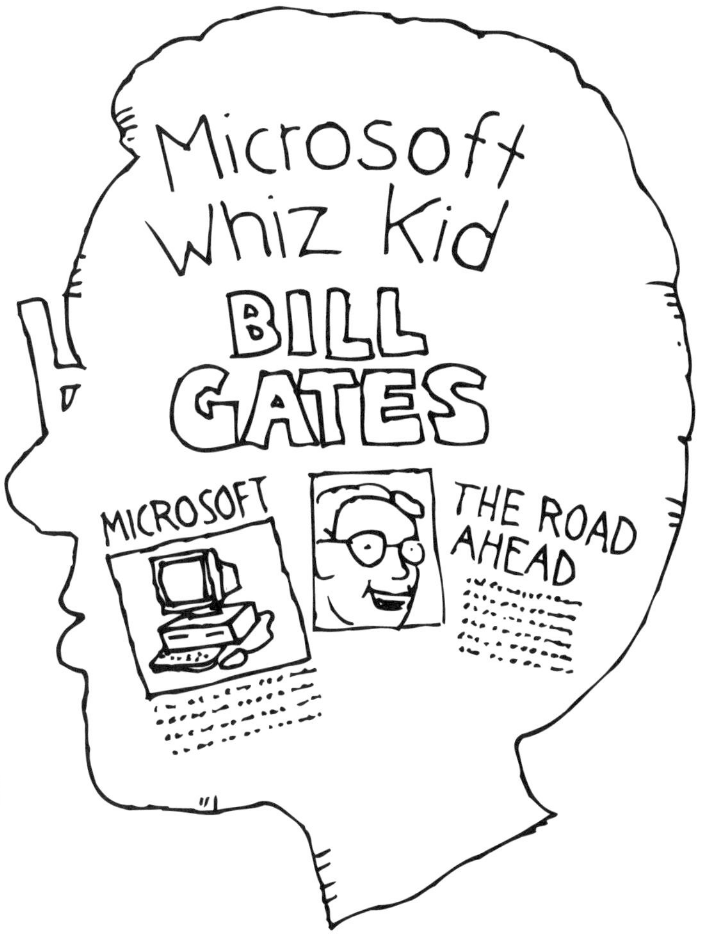

Sharing the Profiles

Provide time for students to present their profiles to the class. They should be able to tell the area of endeavor for which the person is noted and several additional pieces of information.

Public Opinion Poll

News organizations often conduct public opinion polls to find out how the populace views certain issues, events, or situations. Look for results of polls in newspapers and magazines. (*U.S.A. Today* has one in every issue.) Reproduce some on transparencies to introduce the concept to your class. After discussing the reasons for and nature of opinion polls, your class can conduct a poll.

Steps to Follow

1. Brainstorm with your class to come up with a topic that is interesting and relates to your curriculum. Discuss a variety of possibilities and choose one.

2. Devise a short list of questions on the subject. Make sure that the questions are clear. It will be easier to tally responses to the poll if there are a limited choice of answers, as in these samples:

Health

Do you exercise regularly? (yes) (no)

What type of exercise do you prefer? (walking) (running) (gym) (other)

How many minutes each week do you exercise? (0) (less than 30) (30–60) (more than 60)

Are you concerned about fat in your diet? (yes) (no)

Have you altered your diet to consume less fat? (a little) (a lot) (not at all)

School

Should students be required to wear uniforms? (yes) (no)

Is the amount of homework currently given (too much) (too little) (about right)?

Do you think that extracurricular activities (such as band and football) are important? (yes) (no) (don't know)

3. Determine how you will choose the sample of people to be polled. It is a good idea to require students to limit their interviews to people they know personally. This will not yield data as accurate as that from a random sample, but safety is of greater importance.

4. Reproduce one copy of the survey sheet on the following page, and fill in your questions. Make enough copies for each student to interview a number of people.

Examining the Results

There are a number of ways to examine the results of your poll(s):

- Ask students to write a paragraph explaining the results.
- Share your results with local news media if the subject is one in which they might have an interest.
- Translate the results of the poll into percentages.
- Display the results in fractions using a pie chart. Break down the data according to the age and gender of the respondents.

Name:

Public Opinion Poll

Background Information About Respondent

 Age: M   F 

1. Question: ______________________________

Answer: ______________________________

2. Question: ______________________________

Answer: ______________________________

3. Question: ______________________________

Answer: ______________________________

4. Question: ______________________________

Answer: ______________________________

5. Question: ______________________________

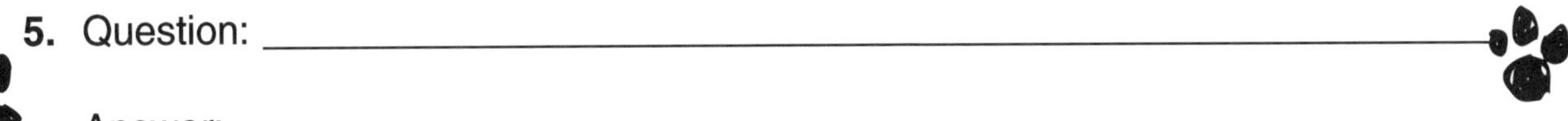

Answer: ______________________________

Comments: ______________________________

____

News Bulletins

News Words
Ask students to read a short newspaper article (two or three paragraphs), underlining or highlighting words whose pronunciation or meaning they are not sure of. Direct students to look up each new word in the dictionary and rewrite the article in their own words. A thesaurus might be helpful.

Compare Coverage
Bring in more than one news magazine for the same week. Compare the coverage of a news event or issue in the two magazines. How does the coverage differ? What emphasis is given in each? Does one magazine seem to be more objective than the other?

Newsmaker of the Month
Near the end of each month, discuss with your class the various men and women who have been in the headlines. Allow students to make nominations for "Person of the Month." Require students who make nominations to support their candidate with reasons why that person should be selected. After discussion of the nominees, take a vote. Post the name of the person of the month on a bulletin board or poster.

Match the Captions
Select ten or twelve interesting pictures with captions from newspapers or magazines. Cut them out. Separate the pictures from the captions. Paste the pictures on a sheet of posterboard and number them. Paste the captions on a smaller sheet of posterboard and assign letters to them. As a center activity, ask students to match the pictures and captions. Provide an answer key for self-correcting.

Newsmaker of the Month

Sir Winston negotiates ceasefire between alley cats and junk-yard dogs.

Make a Newsworthy Puzzle

Creating a crossword puzzle is a lot of fun, but it can be confusing unless you know the basics. Model for your class the steps they will use to create their own puzzles.

Materials (for the model lesson)

- transparency of news article on page 272 (or reproduce for each student)
- transparency of page 273

Materials (for the independent activities)

- page 273, reproduced for each student
- a newspaper or magazine article for each student (assigned by you or chosen by students)

Steps to Follow

1. Read the sample news article together.
2. Explain that the highlighted words are **key** or important words that will be used to create a crossword puzzle. Write these words on the chalkboard.
3. Explain the basic rules of a crossword puzzle:
   - words may go down or across
   - each word must cross over at least one other word
   - wherever letters touch, they must form words
   - clues or definitions are organized across and down
4. Make *cheeseburger* the first word on the transparency grid as shown on the completed puzzle below. Start it in the fifth box down in column one.
5. Lead the class to assist with the remainder of the puzzle or allow them to complete it as they wish.
6. Number the puzzle. Correct crossword numbering starts with the word closest to the upper-left corner and proceeds horizontally. As you come to the place where a word starts (whether across or down), give that box the next number in sequence. (See sample puzzle.)
7. Create definitions or clues for each word in the puzzle.
8. Students read their own news article, highlight key words, and create their own crossword puzzle on the grid provided.

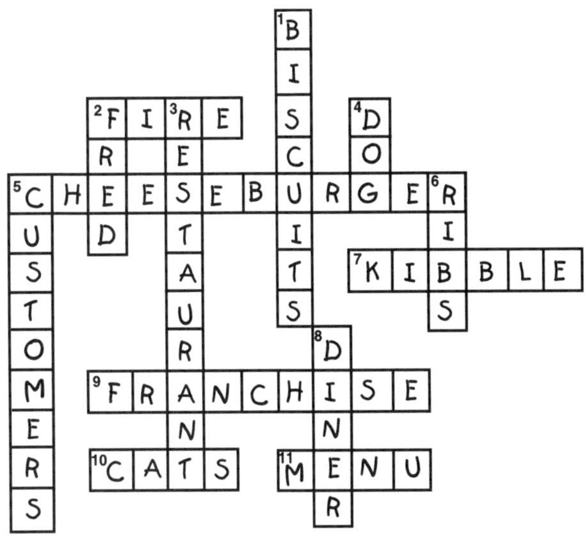

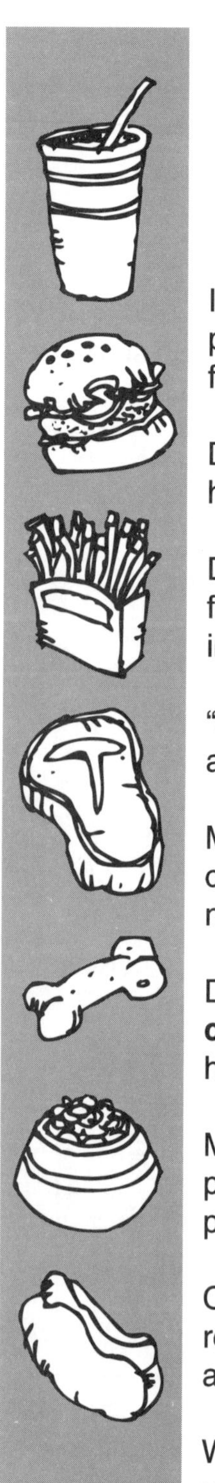

Eating Out

Don't Forget the Family Pet

Is your **dog** looking for more variety in his diet? Is he tired of plain **kibble**? You could get him a very special **cheeseburger**, fries, and a soda.

Doggie Diner, a drive-through **restaurant** for pets, also serves hamsters, **cats**, and monkeys.

Doggie **Diner** serves pet food made with ingredients just like you find in dog **biscuits**, but shaped like people food. The **menu** includes steaks, burgers, and **ribs**.

"Business has been dog-gone great," said owner Tom Miller, 45, a former attorney.

Miller opened the restaurant in Central City in 1990. "I think we can **franchise** this idea and open pet drive-throughs all over the nation."

Doggie Diner even has a fenced playground for its four-legged **customers**, and the building is shaped like a three-story **fire** hydrant.

Miller opened the restaurant after watching his own dog beg for part of his fast-food meals. "I felt kind of guilty and thought that pets ought to have their own special drive-throughs."

Customer Betty Divine says her collie **Fred** loves the trips to the restaurant in the family car. "Fred gets so excited! He wags his tail all the way there and all the way home."

What's the average dinner bill to treat the pet who loves you unconditionally? Around $5.

Name:

Make a Newsworthy Puzzle 2

Make up a crossword puzzle using key words and definitions from a news article. Use the grid on this page to make it easier. Fill in the words you wish to use, making sure each word crosses over at least one other word. Black out all the spaces not used.

Be sure to number the spaces carefully and make sure that the definitions correspond to the numbered spaces.

Write your definitions on another piece of paper. Write all the definitions for the words that go across first. Then write the definitions for the words that go down. Be sure to number the clues the same way you number the puzzle.

The Great Debate

Magazines and newspapers provide an arena in which a variety of voices can analyze and discuss the most current and controversial events and issues of the day. You can use periodical literature as a resource to provide background material for debates among your students.

Participating in a debate provides an excellent way for your students to consider both sides of an issue. Much research, thought, and discussion go into the making of a successful debate.

Choosing a Topic
Perhaps the most important factor is choosing a subject for the debate. Good subjects for debate must be clear and understandable to the debaters as well as to the listeners, have two definite sides, and be stated in the affirmative. Here are some examples:

- All high school sports programs should be eliminated.
- All members of Congress should be limited to two terms in office.
- Vending machines on the school campus should dispense only milk, juice, and fruit.
- The age at which people can obtain a driver's license should be raised to 18.

Establishing Ground Rules
While you may not wish to introduce your students to all the fine points of formal debating, it is helpful to establish some ground rules:

1. There should be an even number of debaters on each team.
2. One person speaks at a time, and there is a time limit on each speaker. (One minute is plenty of time for upper elementary and middle school students.)
3. Affirmative and negative speakers alternate turns, and may answer the arguments of the opposing speaker.
4. Each speaker (or team) should have an opportunity to make a concluding statement.

Forming Teams

Divide your class into teams of four or six. Half of the team will argue one side of the issue; the other half will argue the opposite side. Remind students that they do not have to agree with the position that they take in the debate.

Preparing the Arguments

After teams have chosen their topic to debate, they must look very carefully at the issue, finding all the important arguments on both sides. It is important that they familiarize themselves with both sides so they are prepared for the arguments that will be presented by the opposition. Direct students to list arguments in two columns, labeled "for" and "against."

Students may need help locating magazine and newspaper articles that present two sides of an issue. Enlist assistance from the school and public librarians. Allow students several class periods to study their issue and to prepare their arguments.

Conducting the Debate

When a group is ready, schedule a time for the debate and set up chairs or tables in the front of the room.

Assign a student to act as timer. Review the rules of the debate.

Remind the audience that they will be the ones to determine the outcome of the debate, so they should listen carefully and make notes if desired.

When the debate concludes, take a vote of the audience to determine which team did a more effective job at presenting their side of the argument.

Name:

A Real Role Model

A **role model** is someone who behaves in a way that demonstrates important values. This is a person whose actions often inspire others to do what is right.

Find an article in a magazine or newspaper about someone you think is a good role model for others. Use the information in the article to create a drawing showing how that person acts as a role model. Make sure that your drawing clearly demonstrates this person's contribution. Then write a paragraph explaining your picture.

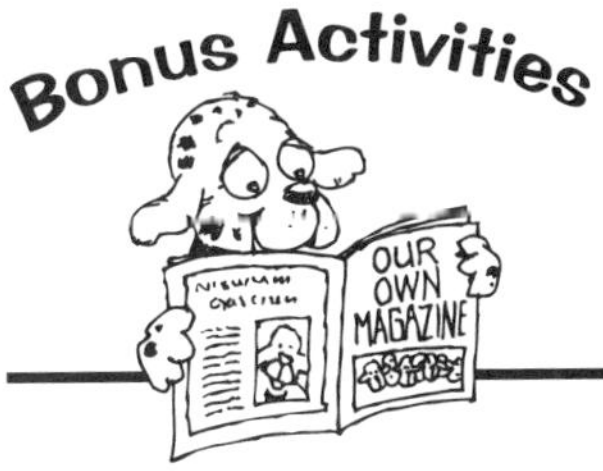

Bonus Activities

Name:

Word Search

S T N E M E S I T R E V D A D N
C L A S S I F I E D A D S R O O
H A B C D E Z T S R E I M O T I
U S A R T I C L E D A Z T I O T
M G P N R E T R O P E R L E R A
A N S P O R T S T I A L G E S M
N I Z N O I T P A C I S P D I R
I D N T L A T E L Y W A F I O O
N A T A O O N A L E P A D T S F
T E M C T D C U N S P T I O I N
E H A A K I H A W R E D F R D I
R R G E T O O E L T E D O I E A
E E A I W E N N C O V T M A B Z
S V L S P T S C A P O O I L A I
T O M Y C H E A D L I N E N R N
P C T M A G A Z I N E N A M O E

Find these newspaper and magazine words in the puzzle.

advertisements
article
caption
classified ads
cover
editor
editorial

headings
headline
human interest
information
local
magazine

national
news
newspaper
political cartoon
reporter
sidebar
sports

Reading Newspapers and Magazines Skills Checklist ✓

	Student's Names								
Newspapers									
Identifies sections of the newspaper									
Identifies the 5 W's in an article									
Understands the use of headlines									
Writes a short article using the 5 W's									
Reads information on weather charts									
Finds information in classified ads									
Experiences using microfiche records									
Participates in creating a newspaper									
Shows interest in reading the newspaper									
Magazines									
Identifies various aspects of magazines									
Creates a magazine cover with necessary information									
Uses a magazine table of contents									
Evaluates advertisements									
Reads a magazine article for information using:									
headings									
key words									
captions									
maps/charts/diagrams									
Participates in creating a classroom magazine									
Shows interest in reading magazines for information and enjoyment									

Answer Key

Page 5

1. the reservoir
2. chlorine to kill germs; fluoride for strong teeth
3. alum is added; mud and dirt sticks to it and sinks to the bottom. in the mixing basin
4. mixing basin; settling basin; filter; storage tank
5. Answers will vary, but should address the idea that unpurified water could spread disease.

Page 6

100-Yard Dash

Place
5
4
2
3
1
6

High Jump

Number	Place
8	1
30	2
18	6
19	3
20	5
39	4

Page 7

Pole Vault

Number	Place
25	1
18	5
15	4
22	2
10	5
12	3

Shot Put

Number	School	Place
19	Taylor	1
11	Taylor	3
46	Anderson	6
20	Anderson	2
28	Taylor	5
15	Anderson	4

Page 8

Anderson High School

1st place wins: 1
2nd place wins: 3
3rd place wins: 0

1st place points: 5
2nd place points: 9
3rd place points: 0
Total points: 14

Taylor High School

1st place wins: 3
2nd place wins: 1
3rd place wins: 4

1st place points: 15
2nd place points: 3
3rd place points: 4
Total points: 22

1. Taylor, by 8 points
2. Anderson: Washington, Fernandes, Nguyen
   Taylor: Rashad, Brenner, Yee
3. Washington, 8
4. Answers will vary.

Page 12

Best Buy Catalog

Jeffrey A. O'Brien — (523) 787-3344
Name: First / Middle Initial / Last — Area Code / Telephone

44 Washington Avenue, Oakville, CA 97655
Address / City / State / Zip Code

Item	Catalog Number	Weight	Size	Color	Price
1 Safe-Landing	L69398	2.20	—	—	18.69
2 Dial-a-Size Helmet	M89356	2.80	—	?	41.20
3 Lightning In-Line	C97321	8.0	8	—	51.98
4		13.0			

Total price of order: 111.87
Sales tax (8%): 8.95
Total weight: 13.0 — Shipping and handling: 12.50
Amount owed: 133.32

Page 13

1. He will receive two protective packs. There is a protective pack that comes with the skates he ordered and one set he ordered separately.
2. He could return the protective pack he ordered and keep the one that came with the skates.
3. Jeffrey's refund would be $23.88—$18.69+$1.50+$3.69. (cost of the merchandise x .08 sales tax + $3.69 for postage). Since the shipping charge is the same for all orders between 10 and 19.9 pounds, Jeffrey would not receive a refund for shipping and handling.
4. about 30 days
5. Read the descriptions more carefully.
6. Answers will vary.

Page 15

1. Read the directions.
   Make sure all the parts listed are in the package.
   See what tools you will need.
   Set up a toolbox.
2. wood glue, screwdriver, towel, hammer
3. 1 back, 2 sides, 3 shelves, 12 wooden pegs, 18 screws

Page 16

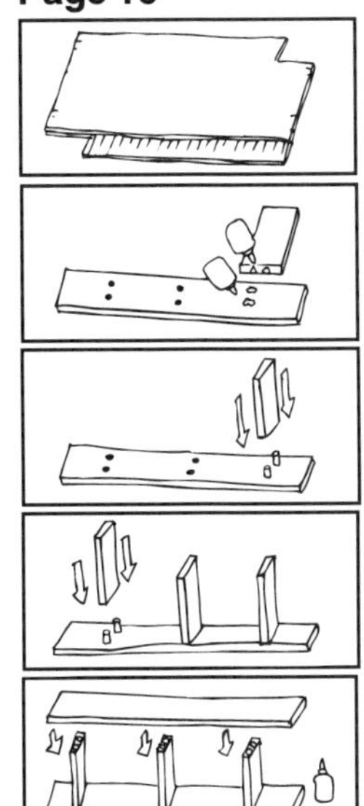

Page 17

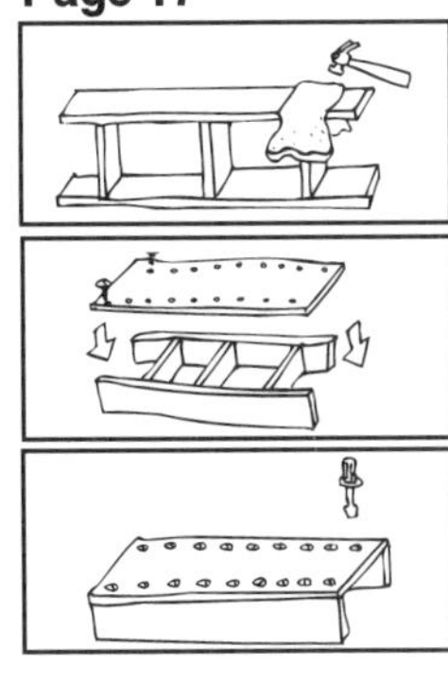

Page 18
If you wish to move a mountain, carry away a few stones at a time.

Page 20
1. B **2.** D **3.** F **4.** A **5.** E **6.** G **7.** C

Page 23
1. Tina Allen 555-4261
2. 566 Oak 555-1111
3. 4 people
4. Green Ave.
5. Sam
6. Chicken 'n Chips, Doggie Pals Pet Shop, Fun and Games Toy Shop
7. Berry's Ice-Cream Parlor on 6th
8. 555-6200

Page 25
1. pet stores
2. names of stores, addresses, phone numbers, what store provides, when the store is open
3. 555-5571
4. animal supplies, animal grooming
5. 11-5 M-F, 11-1 Sat, Sun
6. Tropical Fish & Birds
7. First Street
8. Park Place Wash-a-Pet OR Pet Place

Page 29
1. 3 months
2. 1 day
3. Another student will substitute.
4. sell, put away merchandise, keep records, make up missed class work.
5. 40 minutes
6. Answers will vary, but may include: use good manners, be polite, make suggestions, smile.
7. $2.40

Page 33
1. Three of the following:
   parent must notify if someone else is picking up a camper
   photo I.D. for people picking up camper
   emergency phone numbers
   medications listed
   allergies and health information listed
   list of any activities camper can't take part in
2. to make sure the camper stays healthy and safe
3. parent or guardian
4. May 1

Page 35
Errors on application:
1. name listed in the wrong order
2. left out the name of the state
3. had not graduated when he turned in the application
4. he will be a college student in the fall
5. he mixed up previous work experience and the job he would like to have
6. he needs to explain that he wants full-time work in the summer and weekends in the fall
7. he can't work without a permit until July 1

1. after July 1
2. Palma, Martin Antonio
3. Answers will vary.
4. I would like to work full-time during the summer, and one day a weekend starting in the fall.

Page 39
1. March 1
2. no
3. fill out the information at the bottom of the entry blank, turn it in at the counter, and rent a movie
4. hundreds
5. answers will vary.
6. a free candy bar with your next movie rental

Page 40
1. proof-of-purchase seals from 5 boxes, entry blank on the back of the box, and register receipts
2. You have to subtract the cost of the postage from the amount of the rebate. You could lose money.
3. by July 20
4. eight weeks after July 20

Page 42
Fluffy - 3
Sam's Pizza - 4
Sneakers - 1
Glow Toothpaste - 2

Page 45
Marked diagram of remote control for **(1–4)**

5. Press the PAUSE button again.
6. "0430"
7. Press the PROG button.
8. Put in the tape, press RECORD, press the VCR button to turn it off. Select a channel on the TV.

Page 46

1. garlic, onion, carrot, zucchini
2. Five of the following: onion, carrot, zucchini, beans, tomatoes, spinach
3. Italian seasoning, water, chicken broth, tomatoes
4. 28 minutes
5. water

Page 48

1. Cereal A
2. Vitamin A, zinc, riboflavin
3. Vitamins C, B_{12}, E, copper, phosphorus, thiamin
4. Vitamin B_6, iron, magnesium, niacin
5. calcium, potassium
6. Answers will vary. Students should name Cereal A because it is lower in fat and sugar, higher in fiber, and has a higher vitamin and mineral content.

Page 50

1. Answers will vary.
2. Super Cheeseburger 106
   Deluxe Cheeseburger 64
   Fish Sandwich 68
   Chicken Supreme 29
3. Chicken Supreme

Page 51

6, 6, 5, 12, 6, 4, 6, 6, 11 or 9, 3

Page 54

Materials needed:

centimeter graph paper, ruler, pencil, scissors, cardboard or posterboard, felt pens or crayons, tape, glue, wooden skewer, construction paper

Shopping list:

centimeter graph paper
cardboard or posterboard
felt pens or crayons
wooden skewer
construction paper

Page 57

Name of Plant	Size	Bloom or Harvest Time
Gladiolus	18–24"	Spring–Fall
Daffodil	varies	Spring
Tulip	10–12"	Spring
Snapdragon	6"–4 ft.	Winter–Spring
Forget-Me-Not	6–12"	Late Spring–Fall
African Daisy	12–18"	Late Fall–Early Spring
Wallflower	1–2 1/2 ft.	Feb.–May
Chrysanthemum	2–3 ft.	June–Late Summer
Shasta Daisy	1–3 ft.	June–Late Summer
Sneeze-Weed	6 ft.	August and September
Pincushion	2 1/2 ft.	May–December
Larkspur	3–4 ft.	Spring
Sunflower	7–10 ft.	Summer and Fall
Zinnia	1/2–3 ft.	Summer and Fall
Lettuce	Under 1 ft.	Winter, Spring
Cabbage	12–18"	Spring, Late Fall
Tomato	2–4 ft.	Late Summer and Fall
Corn	6–8 ft.	Fall
Asparagus	Under 1 ft.	Spring
Broccoli	1–2 ft.	Winter
Pumpkin	1 1/2–2 ft.	Fall
Carrot	tops 9–12"	cool season
Pea	3 ft.	Winter, Spring
String bean	3 ft.	Summer

Page 58

Choices will vary. Let students evaluate each other's responses.

Page 60

1. The information said she carries a heavy load of books. The advertisement states it holds up to only 6 pounds.
2. The load of books was too heavy for the bag.
3. A19 - all-weather, padded straps, water bottle strap
4. A18 - overnighter backpack, extra-strength straps, strap for sleeping bag

Page 62

Symbols will vary.

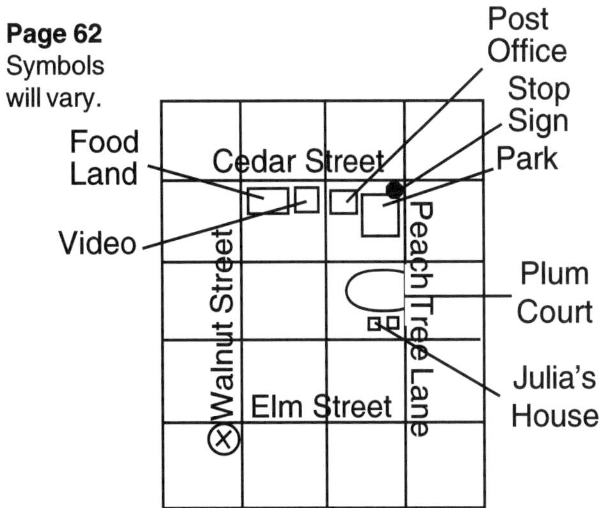

Page 63

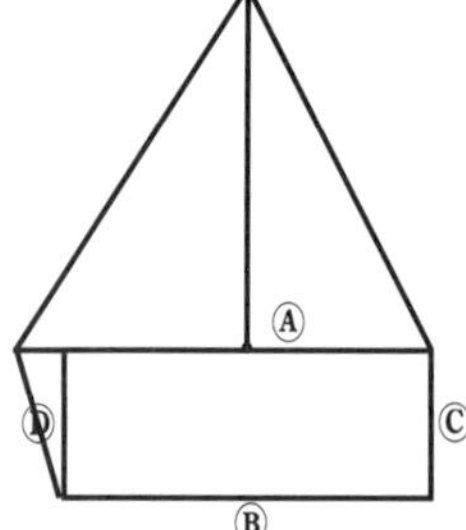

Page 73

1. 6:30 p.m.
2. 4 hours
3. 1½ hours
4. Accept any reasonable answers.
5. beach hike—3½ hours
6. around 12:00
7. Accept any reasonable answers.
8. 1 hour

Page 78

1. Who burned the White House?
   English troops under General Ross and Admiral Cockburn
2. What happened?
   Soldiers piled everything in the middle of the rooms; set things on fire; gunpowder exploded; the White House was destroyed.
3. Where did the White House burn?
   in Washington City
4. When did the White House burn?
   August 24, 1814
5. Why was the White House burned?
   The United States and Great Britain were at war.

Page 81

1. cuckoo family
2. loose feathers, strong bill, tail longer than body, 1st & 4th toes point backward, brown & buff, line on cheek blue to orange
3. rattlesnakes, grasshoppers, birds' eggs, centipedes, scorpions, tarantulas, horned toads, mice, small rats, fruits, seeds, lizards.
4. desert
5. nests in high spot in cactus or bushes; made of snake skins, sticks, dry manure flakes, feathers
6. X
7. X
8. hunts rattlesnakes, likes walking better than flying

Page 83

(First word in the sentence and the number)
Matthew - 1
His mother - 3
He moved - 3
His uncle - 3, 4
At thirteen - 3
The captain - 4
He traveled - 4
Wherever - 4
Later - 5
Finally - 5
He was - 5
Peary - 5
In June - 5
They explored - 5
Henson was a valuable - 5
He worked - 5
Henson was the co-discoverer - 5

Page 87

1. (Underlined) There is a list with the last names of the authors, another one with book titles, and a list of subjects.
2. (Circled) use letters for different subjects.
3. (Boxed) has a system of numbers.
4. (A triangle in front of) Biographies and autobiographies are shelved alphabetically by the person's last name.

1. Dewey decimal system
2. microfilm and microfiche
3. by author, book title, and subject
4. reference section

Page 88

1. Chapter 3
2. Chapter 6
3. Chapter 5
4. Chapter 4, 5
5. Chapter 2
6. Chapter 4

Inside the Chapter

1. Chapter 4
2. Chapter 6
3. Chapter 5

Page 89

1. 14, 26
2. 7, 15–18
3. 8, 18–20
4. 14
5. 1–2, 12, 16, 27
6. 1–2, 13, 15, 26

Page 90

(Circled) The echidna is a spiny anteater that lives in Australia.
(Underlined) long, thin snout, a small mouth, short legs, spines on back and sides; brown; Between its spines it has stiff hairs, toes on hind feet have long claws.

Page 91

1. Sam Martin
2. final score, Washington 41 Barkley 7
3. Washington, touchdowns, last quarter, two
4. name, Washington, team, Scorpions
5. caught five passes, Alan Baker

Page 92

1. age 10
2. fireman for the railroad
3. mechanical engineering
4. Bell Telephone, telephone transmitter
5. improve train safety, developed a train telegraph system so moving trains would know when another train was on the track
6. brakes, automatic air brakes

Page 95

1. The Amazon River in South America is one of the world's great rivers.
2. The Amazon has more tributaries than any other river in the world.
3. Each day the Amazon deposits tons of food-laden silt in the ocean.

Page 96

Black Bears

Black bears are the smallest bears in North America.

Black bears are omnivores.

Page 97

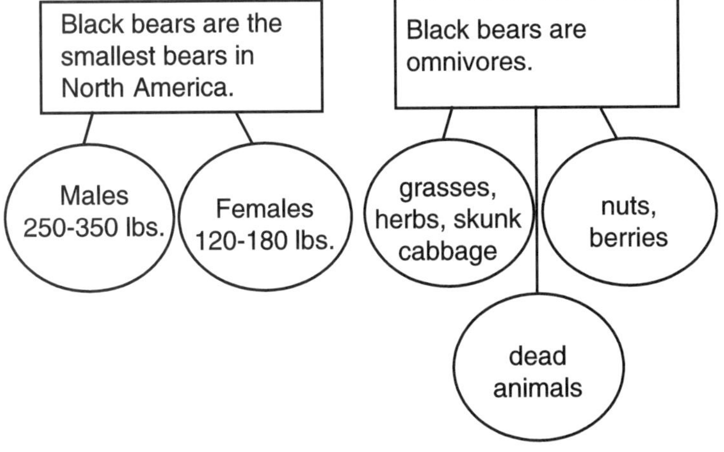

Page 99

Paragraph 1

The eruption of Mount St. Helens on May 18, 1980, caused widespread destruction.
- steam, rock 60,000 feet up
- lightning, flaming cinders caused forest fires
- Spirit Lake a mass of mud, debris
- mud, debris covered roads, bridges, buildings

Paragraph 2

Signs of the explosion traveled long distances.
- blocked out sunlight in Spokane, Washington
- volcanic dust as far as Virginia

Page 102

1, 8, 4, 2, 7, 3, 5, 6

Page 103

3, 8, 7, 4, 1, 6, 2, 5, 9

Page 105

Possible events and dates:

Became interested in newspapers 1718
Wrote funny stories for brother's newspaper 1722
Published *Pennsylvania Gazette* 1729
Invented the Franklin Stove 1741
Proved lightning was electricity 1752
Organized a better mail-delivery system 1753
Went to England to work for freedom for colonies 1757
Convinced England to end the Stamp Act 1766
Signed Declaration of Independence 1776
Became minister to France 1776
Helped write peace treaty with England 1782
Invented bifocal glasses 1783
Member of Constitutional Convention 1787
Died in Philadelphia 1790

Page 110

1. X born in 1867
8. X patients mistreated, many didn't belong there
11. X traveled by ship, train, sampan, horse, burro, stagecoach, jinricksha
12. X returned in 72 days, 6 hours, 11 minutes, and 14 seconds
13. X married millionaire, Robert Seaman, 1895

14–16 may include three of the following:
ran his manufacturing plant after he died
business failed
interned in Europe during World War I
died January 27, 1922

Page 111

2. Sojourner Truth spoke against slavery, visited President Lincoln
3. moon smaller than earth, grayish rocks, dust
4. koalas, "no drink" in Aborigine, eucalyptus forests NE, SE Australia coast
5. peanuts - tasty, healthful, used in soap, face powder, shaving cream, shampoo, paint
6. Columbus - sail around globe to prove earth sphere, not flat
7. rhinoceros rests in day, active at night, eats grass, twigs, shrubs

Page 112

1. made of ice, dirt, and rock
2. coma (tail) is gas
3. coma (tail) million miles long
4. loses dust and gas, gets smaller
5. some visit sun once, others return
6. Halley's every 76 years
7. Halley's next trip 2061

Page 114

Order may vary.

A. Digs up nests and homes of insects
B. Pulls out insects with long, sticky tongue
C. Crushes food in mouth - no teeth
D. Grains of dirt it scoops up help grind its food

Page 116

The details on page 115 should be written in the circles under the same heading.

Page 117

- **I.** Early life
  - **A.** Born in Africa
  - **B.** Captured, brought to America as a slave when 8 or 9
  - **C.** Bought by John Wheatley in Boston
- **II.** Life as a slave
  - **A.** Companion for Wheatley twins, Mary and Nathaniel
  - **B.** Helped Mrs. Wheatley, an invalid
  - **C.** Taught to read and write
  - **D.** Given freedom in 1772 when about 20
- **III.** Her poetry
  - **A.** Wrote first poem at age 13
  - **B.** Wrote poem for Mary's wedding
  - **C.** People in Boston wanted poems written for them
  - **D.** Traveled to England where her poems were published, 1773
- **IV.** Her later life
  - **A.** Married John Peters
  - **B.** Had three children, two died
  - **C.** Husband taken to debtor's prison
  - **D.** She and her baby died in December 1784

Page 119

rises 33,476 feet from ocean floor
only 13,796 feet is above sea level
snow near the summit

Page 120

B. **1.** active

C. **1.** world's highest volcano
2. rises 33,476 feet from ocean floor
3. 13,796 feet above sea level
4. snow near summit

Page 124

Parts of a Leaf (Crossed out)**:**
roots are another part of the plant
a bulb is an underground stem
leaves have many sizes and shapes

The Octopus (Crossed out)**:**
Clams are mollusks that have two shells.
Many sea animals can be found on the ocean floor.
Its relative the squid has ten tentacles.
Slugs are an example of land mollusks.
The shipworm is a mollusk with a different menu. It eats into the wood on piers and boats.
Squids shoot out a dark liquid too.
The rocks in the sea also serve as hideouts for the moray eel.
Squids often swim in large schools for protection.

Page 126

X The flat-headed frog can survive without water for long periods of time.

X Alice didn't have enough time to finish her science report Friday morning.

Selection three - Answers will vary. For example, if manatees are not protected, they could become extinct.

Page 127

Answers will vary. For example,
Many people led better lives because of Jane Addams' work at Hull House.

Page 128

X Spider webs come in many shapes and uses.

X Central Park offers many choices for recreational activities.

Page 129

Sample answer: Alberta, Canada, has many interesting places to see.

Sample answer: A Venus's-flytrap is a strange plant that grows in North Carolina. Because the soil doesn't have enough food in it, the plant traps and digests insects.

Page 130

X A monkey would not make a good pet.

The Marsh Mosquito sample answer: The marsh mosquito is a health problem.

Page 131

The Marsh Mosquito sample answer: Birds and animals in the marsh need the marsh mosquito to survive.

Mosquito Control sample answer: If water storage containers were closed there wouldn't be as many mosquitoes.

Generalization from all 3 articles, sample answer: The marsh mosquito will not be as big a problem if there are enough birds and animals in the marsh to eat them, and if people cover their water containers.

Page 134

Protection	Body	Food	Size
changes color	horny beak eight tentacles	eats fish	grows to 30 feet in diameter

Page 144

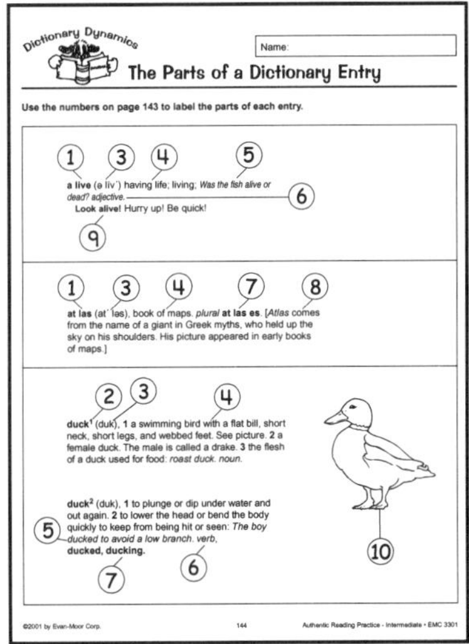

Dictionary Dynamics

Name:

The Parts of a Dictionary Entry

Use the numbers on page 143 to label the parts of each entry.

a live (ə līv′) having life; living; *Was the fish alive or dead? adjective.*
Look alive! Hurry up! Be quick!

at las (at′ ləs), book of maps. *plural* **at las es**. [*Atlas* comes from the name of a giant in Greek myths, who held up the sky on his shoulders. His picture appeared in early books of maps.]

duck[1] (duk), **1** a swimming bird with a flat bill, short neck, short legs, and webbed feet. See picture. **2** a female duck. The male is called a drake. **3** the flesh of a duck used for food: *roast duck. noun.*

duck[2] (duk), **1** to plunge or dip under water and out again. **2** to lower the head or bend the body quickly to keep from being hit or seen: *The boy ducked to avoid a low branch. verb,* **ducked, ducking.**

 144 Authentic Reading Practice - Intermediate • EMC 3301

Page 145

1 carrot	**coop**	**cord**
core	custard	**copilot**
corduroy	climb	contest
2 **gown**	**grain**	gopher
graduate	**grape**	**granny**
graze	gnaw	**governor**
3 **pelican**	**peanut**	**peek**
parakeet	penguin	**peck**
peculiar	pepper	**peacock**

4 **time**	thunder	tomb
tiny	**tight**	table
tinfoil	tiptop	**timber**

Page 146

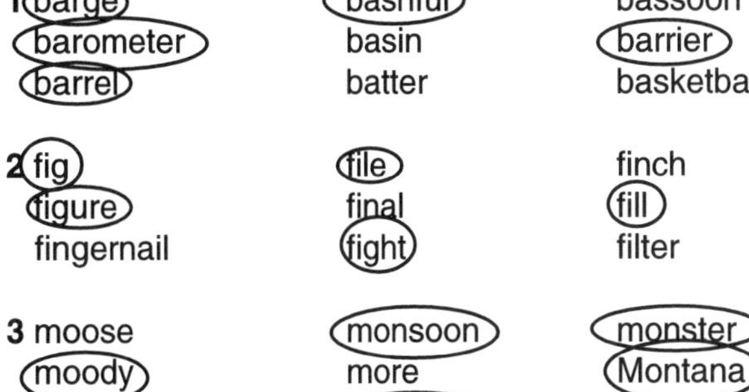

1 **barge**	**bashful**	bassoon
barometer	basin	**barrier**
barrel	batter	basketball
2 **fig**	**file**	finch
figure	final	**fill**
fingernail	**fight**	filter
3 moose	**monsoon**	**monster**
moody	more	**Montana**
monarch	**monopoly**	motor
4 rainbow	ram	raise
rage	**radish**	rajah
raisin	**rafter**	**ragweed**

Page 147

Pictures will vary, but must represent:

pitcher	hawk	goose
eyebrow	faucet	suitcase
orange	moths	canoe

Page 148

1. 1
2. 5
3. 2
4. 4
5. 9
6. 6
7. 7
8. 3

Sentences will vary.

Page 152
1. a plane to level wood
2. a spanner to tighten or loosen a bolt or hose coupling
3. a clutch to shift gears
4. sutures to sew up an incision
5. a pseudonym to write under another name
6. leavening to make dough rise
7. a brief to present a written argument for his/her case
8. a creel to store his fishing equipment

Page 153
1. a ledger to record income and expenses
2. an incantation to perform magic
3. a lariat to rope a cow
4. a sextant to determine position
5. gills to breathe
6. a pane to replace a broken section of window
7. a cistern to collect rainwater
8. a scepter to symbolize his authority

Page 154
1. a bassinet to sleep in
2. a mast to hold up the sails
3. a score to direct the musicians
4. a berth to sleep in
5. a dibble to make holes for planting
6. cement to hold bricks and stones together
7. an anvil to shape horseshoes
8. fescue to provide food for livestock

Page 155
1. an armature to support what is being modeled
2. a filibuster to delay vote on a bill
3. a roux to prepare a cream sauce
4. a rebuttal to counter the opponents' viewpoint
5. a buttress to support a wall
6. spinnerets to produce silk
7. a caret to show where a word should be inserted
8. a bow to play the instrument

Page 156
1. a cleaver to cut meat
2. a barometer to tell the air pressure
3. a gavel to call for order
4. talons to grasp its prey
5. shears to cut hair
6. pigments to paint different colors
7. chambray to make a shirt
8. a quiver to hold the arrows

Page 157
No Legs
conger
anaconda
mullet
amoeba
maggot
Two Legs
executive
mandarin
hombre
puffin
grackle
Four Legs
dromedary
newt
hyrax
Gila monster
okapi
More Legs
hornet
tick
scorpion
centipede
arachnid

Page 158
Build It
pagoda
buttress
spire
minaret
turret
Plant It
palmetto
flax
narcissus
columbine
begonia
Eat It
repast
morsel
rusk
ambrosia
victuals
Wear It
gauntlet
sari
tiara
beret
monocle

Page 159
Float
sloop
dory
junk
kayak
sampan
yawl
skiff
Roll
hansom
sulky
trolley
jalopy
ricksha
perambulator
buggy
Fly
dirigible
airship
glider
Slide
sledge
travois
toboggan

Page 160
Noisy
calliope
din
bellow
clamor
piccolo
Quiet
muffle
mute
sedate
mime
stealthy
Hot
singe
tropical
kiln
forge
magma
Cold
rime
tundra
frigid
floe
arctic

Page 161
Dog
canine
mongrel
cur
jackal
Cat
lynx
feline
ocelot
calico
tabby
Cow
bovine
cud
heifer
ruminant
low
dewlap
Horse
equine
foal
filly
dun
roan

Page 162

Page 163

Page 164

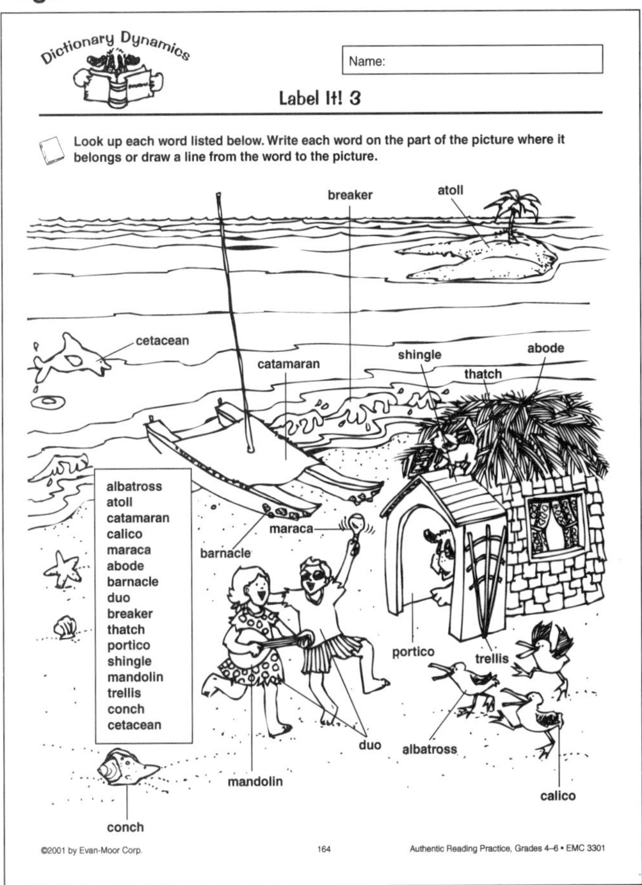

Page 165

Page 166

Dictionary Dynamics

Name:

Label It! 5

Look up each word listed below. Write each word on the part of the picture where it belongs or draw a line from the word to the picture.

adder
condor
adobe
butte
aliment
festoon
digit
hominy
maize
madras
saguaro
salutation
canine
parcel
portal
ceramic

©2001 by Evan-Moor Corp. 166 Authentic Reading Practice, Grades 4–6 • EMC 3301

Page 167

1. chocolate
2. cookie
3. recipe
4. favorite
5. dessert
6. flour
7. sugar
8. vanilla
9. margarine
10. grease
11. minutes
12. delicious

Page 168

1. Accepts
2. enough
3. honor
4. excited
5. optimistic
6. actually
7. medal
8. humble
9. among
10. succeed
11. dedication
12. chief
13. committee
14. license
15. Professor
16. guarantee
17. exceed
18. expectations

Page 169

1. friend
2. eighth
3. February
4. beginning
5. bicycle
6. expedition
7. across
8. arctic
9. ridiculous
10. everything
11. necessary
12. success
13. doctor
14. pneumonia
15. sacrifice
16. history
17. confidence
18. all right
19. Sincerely

Page 170

1. Bulletin
2. ninth
3. thief
4. neighborhood
5. jewelry
6. occasion
7. counterfeit
8. gems
9. chauffeur
10. millionaire
11. innocent
12. laboratory
13. examine
14. scene
15. business
16. expense
17. answer
18. mystery
19. minute

Page 171

1. diary
2. You'll
3. guess
4. happened
5. drawer
6. opened
7. flew
8. straight
9. tried
10. pretend
11. furious
12. couldn't
13. laughing
14. insist
15. principal
16. tomorrow
17. sense
18. humor

Page 277

Bonus Activities

Name:

Word Search

S T N E M E S I T R E V D A D N
C L A S S I F I E D A D S R O O
H A B C D E Z T S R E I M O T I
U S A R T I C L E D A Z T I O T
M G P N R E T R O P E R L E R A
A N S P O R T S T I A L G E S M
N I Z N O I T P A C I S P D I R
I D N T L A T E L Y W A F I O O
N A T A O O N A L E P A D T S F
T E M C T D C U N S P T I O I N
E H A A K I H A W R E D F R D I
R R G E T O O E L T E D O I E A
E E A I W E N N C O V T M A B Z
S V L S P T S C A P O O I L A I
T O M Y C H E A D L I N E N R N
P C T M A G A Z I N E N A M O E

Find these newspaper and magazine words in the puzzle.

advertisements	headings	national
article	headline	news
caption	human interest	newspaper
classified ads	information	political cartoon
cover	local	reporter
editor	magazine	sidebar
editorial		sports

©2001 by Evan-Moor Corp. 277 Authentic Reading Practice - Intermediate • EMC 3301